BACKYARD PHYSICS

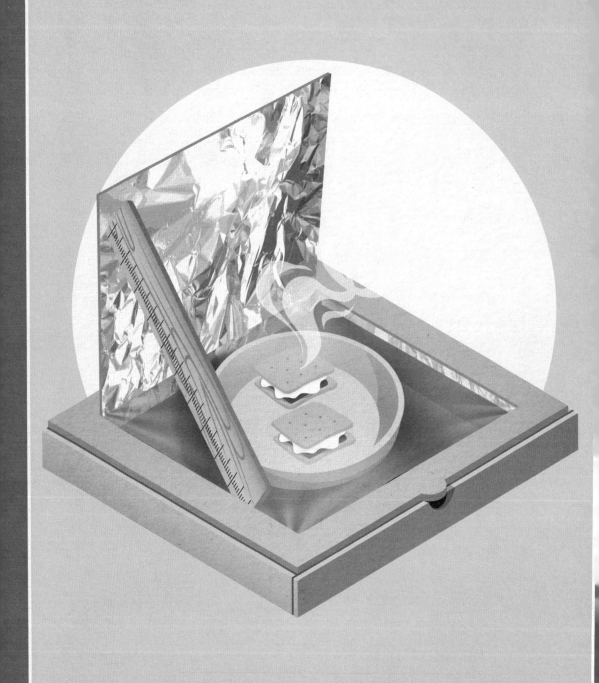

BACKYARD PHYSICS

INCREDIBLE EXPERIMENTS
WITH EVERYDAY OBJECTS

CHARLES PHILLIPS

METRO BOOKS
New York

METRO BOOKS
New York

An Imprint of Sterling Publishing
1166 Avenue of the Americas
New York, NY 10036

METRO BOOKS and the distinctive Metro Books logo
are registered trademarks of Sterling Publishing Co., Inc.

© 2019 Quarto Publishing plc

Original images © 2019 Shutterstock

ISBN 978-1-4351-6991-3

For information about custom editions, special sales, and premium
and corporate purchases, please contact Sterling Special Sales
at 800-805-5489 or specialsales@sterlingpublishing.com.

Manufactured in China

2 4 6 8 10 9 7 5 3 1

sterlingpublishing.com

Design, illustration, and image editing by Amazing15

Science consultant: Melanie Frances

"Don't study science. Play with it."
– Abhijit Naskar

CONTENTS

PART 1

BANGS AND BURNS

PART 2

NATURAL WONDERS

PART 3

SPLASH

PART 4

TRICKS OF LIGHT AND WEIGHT

PART 5

FUTURE SHOCK AND SIMPLY WEIRD

INTRODUCTION

Do you have a little of the mad scientist in you? Maybe we all do. When we're young, we enjoy taking things apart to see how they work or experimenting to see what happens when we mix things together. As adults, we love bangs and flashes and amazing effects. Many of us will recognize thoughts such as, "How did I do that?" "How is it possible—why don't the eggs break?" "That's neat—I didn't get wet!" or "Wow, look at those colors!"

You may not want to go all the way, like Professor Philip Brainard in the movies *The Absent-Minded Professor* and *Flubber*, who was so driven by his passion for science that he missed his own wedding—three times! But if you read on, you'll be amazed to discover how much fun you can safely have with science in your own backyard.

We even have our own version of Professor Brainard's crazy flubber, the difficult-to-control green goo that gets faster when it bounces. Our version (see page 132) is made from household ingredients, and the instructions will enable you to make enough to keep a bunch of people laughing and playing outside.

The book is divided into five chapters, beginning with a collection of our loudest demonstrations: **BANGS AND BURNS**. Here you'll find out how to *safely* make an incombustible banknote that burns but is not consumed, how to produce a controlled fire using water, or how to fire potato pellets from a simple tube gun.

The next section, **NATURAL WONDERS**, explains how to make mini lightning or a tornado in a bottle, and how to recreate many other amazing natural phenomena. Check out the demonstration on how a black hole works, using nothing but some stretchy fabric, a piece of fruit, and a couple of ping-pong balls.

Then in the third chapter, **SPLASH**, we look at liquid wonders and effects. See how to hold a glass of water upside down over your head—and not get wet—or try your hand at making square bubbles.

The fourth chapter, **TRICKS OF LIGHT AND WEIGHT**, focuses on demonstrations linked to light and gravity. Make your own fiber optics or channel the great Renaissance polymath Leonardo da Vinci to build a version of the self-supporting bridge he designed in the 1480s.

Meanwhile, the final chapter, **FUTURE SHOCK AND SIMPLY WEIRD**, covers all sorts, from the hi-tech to the very messy. It will let you in on the secrets of extracting DNA from fruit or walking across a tray of eggs without breaking them.

Having set the scene, let's take a closer look at how the experiments are set out and talk about what you can expect.

ABOUT THIS BOOK

This book contains **50 scientific investigations**, which are often referred to as demonstrations rather than experiments. That's because to conduct a science experiment, you need to perform an action more than once, varying the ingredients and methods to determine exactly what makes a difference. Where there's room in the following pages, we encourage you to try this. Use a different approach to the one first outlined, or test different ingredients or combinations of materials. Note the differences to determine which method or materials work best.

Each experiment follows the same basic structure. It begins with a list of essential materials, which you'll find in the **YOU WILL NEED** section.

The **SETUP** section that follows gives you a simple explanation of how to put these elements together safely.

Next, a paragraph on **TESTING** details how to do the experiment and what you should look for. It also asks pertinent questions, to encourage you and your helpers to get fully involved in working out what is going on.

Where an experiment is more complicated or has variations that will help you dive deeper and discover more, you'll find these in an **ADDITIONAL SETUP** section.

Finally, **IN CONCLUSION** provides notes on the scientific ideas behind the demonstration and, in some cases, their history or everyday applications.

To ensure that you and your family are safe, we provide notes on a few **SAFETY** precautions (page 10). At the back of the book, check out the **GLOSSARY** of key scientific terms (page 154) and some leads on where else to look for fun backyard experiments in **FURTHER READING** (page 156).

That's all there is to it. You're almost ready to hit the backyard and do some physics, professors! First, though, turn the page to read some safety tips.

THROUGHOUT THE BOOK YOU'LL ALSO FIND PUZZLERS TO TEST YOUR SCIENTIFIC KNOWLEDGE. FOR THE ANSWERS TURN TO PAGE 157.

SAFETY

Safety considerations have been paramount in the selection and design of the experiments in this book, and it's always worth taking precautions when you're doing backyard physics. These are simple, sensible steps that will keep your hands and eyes safe, and prevent you scratching, bashing, or burning yourself or others.

CLEAN, TIDY, WELL PREPARED

Read the setup and testing text all the way through before you make a start on an experiment, so that you understand what you'll be doing and can note any safety tips included. Take your time and make sure you're alert. If you've had an alcoholic drink, just enjoy browsing the book and put the actual testing off until another day.

Make sure you have plenty of room on the table and around the area in which you'll be working. Don't let components become crowded together so you risk knocking them over or spilling things.

Keep a first-aid kit handy. Make sure that you've checked it's up-to-date and that you know what's inside and how to use it. Before you embark on any demonstrations that involve fire, make sure you have a working home fire extinguisher or water on hand. Have cleaning materials ready in case you need to clean up spills quickly.

EYES, HAIR, HANDS

If you have safety goggles, that's ideal. If not, cycling glasses can make a good alternative. If you have long hair, always tie it back or pin it up. Wear gloves if you're handling potentially damaging chemicals, and be especially careful when opening your bottle of hydrogen peroxide—never point it at your face or at other people. Finally, never look directly at the sun.

TESTING

Stay alert and take reasonable precautions while you're testing. In the case of the Self-Supporting Bridge (see page 112), for example, check on the structure as you put it together to make sure the pieces are fitting securely, and the first time you cross, go on your hands and knees or ask a friend to hold your hand as you take your first steps. Be careful with any firing or shooting demos, such as the Bottle Rocket (see page 26) and Potato Gun (see page 42)—and make sure no one's in your firing line. Use your potato gun for target practice, not an O.K. Corral-style shootout!

AFTER THE EXPERIMENT

Make sure you put things away safely after testing. In the course of the experiments in this book you may be using a hammer and nails, glasses and jars, a mirror and magnifying glass, balloons, and fishing wire as well as lighting fires and handling hydrogen peroxide. Make sure you put away any tools, blow out any naked flames, and tidy up other materials.

This is particularly important in the case of the Summer Solar Burn-Up demo (see page 20). You must be careful to dismantle the homemade lens, since it can powerfully focus sunlight and could start a fire when you've turned your attention to something else. Similarly, make sure you tidy everything away after Nature's Cookin' (see page 150), another demo that puts the power of the sun to work.

After any of the demos that involve melting ice or handling water, make sure you mop down the affected areas to prevent the risk of a friend or family member slipping over.

You'll also need to be careful when clearing away after the Oobleck Quicksand experiment (see page 48). The cornstarch and water mixture has the extraordinary quality of being both liquid and solid under different conditions—so it could block your pipes and hammer you with a big plumbing bill if you pour it down the drain. It's completely nontoxic and can be safely disposed of in the trash.

SYMBOLS AND WHAT THEY MEAN

 Where we think an experiment demands extra care or has a mild element of danger, you'll see it clearly marked with a DANGER symbol.

 Where we feel there's a chance you're going to create an unholy mess, you'll see the experiment clearly marked with a MESSY symbol.

EQUIPMENT

You don't need any special equipment for the demonstrations in this book. They are designed to be carried out with minimum fuss—but maximum enjoyment—on your own patch and using normal backyard and household equipment. None of the experiments rely on tools or components that are difficult to source or which require lots of complex and fiddly work to put together.

For many of the demonstrations you'll need a table or other work surface in the backyard, for setting up the components, and the common household items listed below.

CLOTHING

Bathing suit

Swim cap

Old clothes

Cotton handkerchief

Piece of stretchy fabric
such as Spandex

Safety goggles or
cycling glasses

HOUSEHOLD/BACKYARD EQUIPMENT

Saucepan

Bowls

Bucket

Drinking glasses

Mortar and pestle

Empty glass jars

Tinfoil

Jug

Tray

Chopstick

Empty soda cans

Empty plastic bottles

Aluminum tray

Plastic wrap

Screwdriver

Tweezers

Coffee filter paper

Empty potato chip tube

Plastic soda bottles

Matches or a lighter

Bicycle pump and
inner tube

Garden spade or fork

Hammer and nails

Magnifying glass

Small mirror

Tablecloth

Cutlery

Plates

Cork

CD

Needle

Magnet

Ruler or measuring tape

Hose

Guitar string or
fishing wire

Freezer bag

Styrofoam™ tray and cups

CRAFT SUPPLIES

Pens and pencils

Ruler

Craft sticks

Craft knife

Scissors

Sticky tape

Pipe cleaners

Rubber bands

Glue

Tissue paper

Pushpins

Balloons

Fishing line
(or guitar string)

Paperclips

Adhesive putty

Glue

PROVISIONS

Cornstarch

Bottle of cola
   (preferably diet)

Mentos® or other candies

Bottle of wine

Dish soap

Watermelon

Yeast

Borax

Food dye

Eggs in their cartons

Sugar cubes

Lettuce

Tubular pasta, e.g. rigatoni
   or ziti

Piece of round fruit
     such as an orange
     or grapefruit

Vegetable oil

Baking soda

Vinegar

Jar of jelly

Water-repellent spray such
   as Scotchgard

Fresh fruit (e.g. pear
   or strawberry)

Potato

MISCELLANEOUS

Ice cubes

Wading pool or
   empty sandbox

Ping-pong balls

Sand

Flashlight

Banknote

Flowers

Candles or tea lights

SPECIAL ORDERS

There are just a couple of experiments where you may need to order items in specially.

WOOD

The Self-Supporting Bridge (see page 112) requires a few lengths of wood cut to size. You may have suitable wood in your shed, but if not it should be possible to source wood from a local supplier. If you can't get ahold of any, or you don't have the space in your backyard to build a large structure, there's an additional setup for this demo that explains how to make the bridge using jumbo craft sticks.

HYDROGEN PEROXIDE

A couple of the experiments— Giant's Toothpaste (see page 32) and Pasta Rocket (see page 38)—ask for hydrogen peroxide. You may have 3% hydrogen peroxide in the house already for use as a disinfectant. This will work for the Pasta rocket but for Giant's toothpaste you'll need a 6 percent solution. You should be able to get this from a drugstore, a beauty supply store, or online.

GLYCERIN

Bouncing bubbles (page 84) calls for glycerin. You can use corn syrup instead if you don't have glycerin or can't track any down, but you should be able to get it at the drugstore or supermarket.

SETTING UP

The experiments in this book are designed to be laid out and performed under the open sky in your backyard. Some are unavoidably—and enjoyably—messy. You wouldn't want Giant's Toothpaste (see page 32) anywhere near your living room carpet or your kitchen furniture. Others rely on outdoor conditions (such as sunlight) or require ventilation. For some, you'll need plenty of room.

Bear in mind a few—largely commonsense—considerations when choosing where in your backyard to carry out the experiments. Some of these points apply to most of the demos; others are more specific.

First, for those experiments that are labeled with the "messy" symbol, choose an area where you don't mind making a major mess. Big-Bang Watermelon (see page 44), for example, will spray bits of fruit all around. You'll probably want to choose a distant corner of the yard, somewhere you'll be happy to get busy with a hose and brush afterward. You might even want to put some plastic sheeting down if, say, your yard is small and you're worried about decking or paving tiles being stained.

Remember that some demonstrations may involve (major) splashing—especially those in the section SPLASH. These are best set up on grass or in an area that has good drainage. You'll probably want to do these experiments on a hot day and to wear either a bathing suit or old clothes.

A few of the experiments are intended not to make a mess but require practice before you can be confident that they won't. For example, you should be able to walk across the eggs in Egg Walk (see page 134), but if you press unevenly or go too slowly it's possible that some eggs will end up broken. Very occasionally, the wine bottle in No Corkscrew? No Problem! (see page 78) may smash if you hit it against the wall at an angle. If this happens, be very careful when you clear up the glass. Also bear potential mess in mind when you first try Vanishing Tablecloth (see page 142). You might need some practice whipping out the tablecloth from beneath the place setting before you start using your best china.

Choose an isolated part of the yard with nothing in the "firing line." A couple of the demonstrations involve sending missiles shooting across the yard or flying powerfully upward—check out Bottle Rocket (see page 26), for instance. Be careful to find a corner where the flying bottle will not hit windows, laundry lines, fences, hothouses, parked vehicles, or anything else. Similarly, when you do the Tube Flip experiment (see page 118) be careful to avoid flying tubes clattering into your backyard shed or furniture.

Make sure you don't get carried away and remember your surroundings. There are other demonstrations, like Potato gun (page 42), which are crazy fun to play with and you might find yourself running around—especially if you've made two spud-zookas and you're going head to head with a family member looking for targets. (Never shoot at people, though!) Here you need to ensure that everyone playing (perhaps younger family members particularly) remembers to keep an eye on what's around them and doesn't let loose where they might hit a window or anything breakable.

For some experiments, Sweet, Sweet Light (see page 110), for example, you'll need a dark corner. Experiments like these work well on an overcast evening when there's little moonlight. Find a spot where there are no streetlights or lights from indoors causing brightness and making the effect more difficult to see. You'll need to get everything ready on the table in the backyard before turning off the outdoor lights.

Some of the demonstrations involve burning, or let off gases as a byproduct, so for these you'll need an open and well-ventilated area. Bear in mind that flames may spread, for example, if you were to drop the flaming banknote in Incombustible Banknote (see page 36). Always keep a fire extinguisher on hand for any experiment involving a naked flame. See the tips on Safety on page 10 before you start setting up any demonstration.

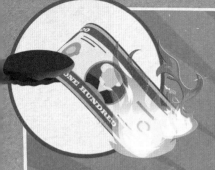

PART 1

BANGS AND BURNS

CONTENTS

COLA VOLCANO

Unleash a fizzy fountain with soda and candy

YOU WILL NEED:
- 68fl oz (2l) bottle of soda, e.g cola (preferably diet) • Roll of Mentos® candies • Piece of paper • Cardstock

This experiment works best with diet soda because the artificial sweetener aspartame, contained in diet drinks, accelerates the process.

SETUP

This will get very messy, so you'll probably want to set it up on a part of your yard where you can wash the stickiness away afterward. Set the full bottle of soda on the ground and remove the lid. Place the cardstock on top of the bottle. Roll up a piece of paper to make a tube that will fit easily in the bottle neck and place it on top of the card stock so that it lines up with the opening of the bottle. Unwrap your roll of candies and drop them into the tube.

TESTING

When you're ready, slide the cardstock away and slot the tube into the bottle neck so the candies fall into it. Then get out of the way as quickly as you can—but don't turn your back or you'll miss the reaction!

What happens if you try a smaller bottle or one made of glass? Does it work as well with a different type of soda—lemonade, seltzer water, or root beer, for example? How about different candies?

IN CONCLUSION

This cola geyser is caused by nucleation—a physical not a chemical reaction. The bottle of soda contains carbon dioxide in solution, under pressure, which is what makes fizzy drinks fizzy. When you open the bottle, and the pressure is released, the carbon dioxide gas precipitates out of this solution, and you see bubbles in the liquid and along the bottle's inner walls. The places where the gas comes out of the solution are called nucleation sites.

Generally, this process is contained, because it takes a lot of energy to happen—activation energy. The Mentos® you drop in have a rough surface because they have been covered with several layers of sugar, and this surface provides many new nucleation sites. The effect is much more nucleation with less activation energy, causing foaming and a jet of liquid driven powerfully upward, thanks to the shape of the bottle. It's even possible to get an eruption 18ft (5.5m) high if it works well.

#2 SUMMER SOLAR BURN-UP

⚠️

Burn, baby, burn!

YOU WILL NEED:
- A hoop, e.g. a sturdy plastic hula hoop or the rim of a small bicycle wheel • Roll of plastic wrap at least 12in (30cm) wide • Water • Two piles of bricks or two patio chairs • Sticky tape • Sunglasses • Cardboard, dry leaves, or other items to burn, melt, or heat

OPTIONAL:
- Different types of plastic wrap • Open-topped wooden or metal frame • Sealable freezer bag

This works best on a summer's day when the sun is high, say, between 10 a.m. and 2 p.m.

SETUP

Take the hoop and stretch the plastic wrap as tightly as possible across it. Secure the plastic wrap around the edge with sticky tape. Try tapping the film surface lightly to check it's as tight as you can get it. Balance the hoop horizontally between two supports, such as two piles of bricks or the seats of two chairs. Use some sticky tape to secure it in position. You should place this over a nonflammable surface—don't put it on the lawn! If you have an area of concrete or tiles in your backyard, that would be ideal. Gently pour water onto the top of the plastic-wrapped hoop. You now have a homemade lens.

TESTING

First, you need to find the focal length of your lens (the distance the lens needs to bring light into sharp focus). You can play around with this by adding or removing water. Adding water decreases the focal length, so you'll need a shorter distance from your lens to the ground for the light to focus. Alternatively, you can raise or lower the lens by adding or removing bricks, changing the chairs, or raising the hoop on both sides using supports. Once you've found the focal length, you'll be able to bring the sun's rays to a sharp point of light. This will be very bright, so you shouldn't look directly at it without first putting on a pair of dark singlasses.

Put some cardboard beneath the point of light. What happens? Try a pile of dry leaves. You could experiment to see what happens with other materials, such as butter, ice cubes, crayons, or a small bowl of water. If you want, you can use a mirror to direct sunlight into the lens—this will be especially useful if the sun is low in the sky.

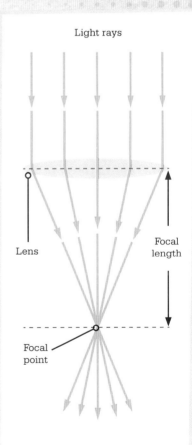

Light rays

Lens

Focal length

Focal point

SUMMER SOLAR BURN-UP

ADDITIONAL SETUP

If you have an open-topped wooden or metal frame, you don't need the hoop; instead, you can tape the plastic wrap directly across the top of the frame. In fact, you can make a lens using all sorts of things. All you need to be able to do is to stretch enough wrap to make a lens around 12in (30cm) wide when you add the water.

You could also try experimenting with the different types of plastic wrap available. What difference do you see if you can get hold of the heaviest-duty type—one designed for catering or for wrapping pallets? If your plastic wrap is thicker you'll be able to add more water to make a deeper, wider lens.

It's also possible to make a lens and start a fire using nothing but a sealable freezer bag and water. First, gather some dry kindling, then simply half-fill the bag with water and use this as a handheld lens to focus sunlight in the same way you might with a small magnifying glass.

IN CONCLUSION

Once the water settles onto the plastic wrap, it exerts uniform pressure across the wrap and forms a "lens" with a smooth surface—the lens is actually the water itself. Your homemade lens focuses the sun's rays on the ground beneath, and the thermal energy in the sunlight is all concentrated into a specific point, generating sufficient heat to start a fire with dry leaves, twigs, or newspaper.

This is a pretty powerful instrument and it can be used for cooking small items. The famous Greek scientist Archimedes even used reflected sunlight as a tool of war. In circa 214 BCE he instructed Syracusan soldiers to reflect sunlight to set Roman ships on fire.

Be careful with fire in your yard and make sure you dismantle the setup once you're done, otherwise your solar lens might start a fire in your backyard when you're not looking!

SUNBEAM LASER

Make a heat weapon using magnified sunlight

YOU WILL NEED:
• Balloon • Marker pen
• Large magnifying glass 2–3in (5–8cm) diameter •
Small mirror around 6in (15cm) diameter • A helper
• Sticky tape
OPTIONAL: Tape measure

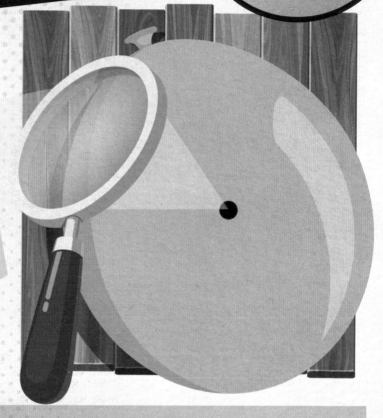

SETUP

Inflate the balloon, draw a large black spot on it about an inch (2.5cm) in diameter, and stick it to a fence or wall in your backyard. Check the focal length of your magnifying glass by shining light from a bright source, such as a flashlight, through the glass and onto a wall. As you move closer to and farther from the wall, you'll see the clarity of the image change. When it's as clear as possible, the light is focused. The distance between you and the wall is the focal length of your lens—typically, around 5in (13cm).

TESTING

Once you know the focal length of your magnifying glass, stand so you are holding it that distance away from the balloon. Ask your helper to use the mirror to reflect sunlight through the lens and onto the black spot.

What happens? Try timing how long it takes. If you have a shed in your backyard, you could check whether the experiment works better indoors, focusing sunlight falling through a window or door. How about if you use a second mirror—so you reflect the sunlight onto the balloon via a relay of two mirrors?

You could even try a version of this experiment using two balloons, one clear and one dark. First, partially inflate the clear balloon and insert the dark balloon inside it, with its opening accessible. Blow up and seal the dark balloon, then fully inflate the clear balloon and seal it. Use your magnifying glass to focus light onto the dark balloon—and get ready!

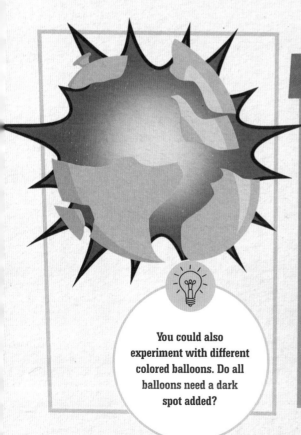

You could also experiment with different colored balloons. Do all balloons need a dark spot added?

IN CONCLUSION

The lens concentrates the thermal energy contained in sunlight. The sun delivers 92W energy per sq ft (1,000W energy/sq m) on a clear day. The dark coloring of the spot you added to the balloon ensures the heat is absorbed by the balloon: dark colors absorb more wavelengths of light and reflect fewer, compared with lighter-colored objects, so more heat is absorbed. The heat then melts the surface of the balloon— which goes out with a bang!

BOTTLE ROCKET

Hand-pumped takeoff

Bike stores will often give away old inner tubes and you can cut the valve from one of these.

SETUP

Check the cork fits snugly in the neck of the bottle. You might need to wind some sticky tape around it to make it a tight fit. Hold the cork upright on a flat surface and use the screwdriver to make a vertical hole through it. Check the inner-tube valve is open and feed it through the hole. (Cut the cork in half if the valve's too short for it.) Then fill the soda bottle about one-quarter full with water and put the cork in. Cut four cardboard triangles and tape them to the top of the bottle, so they point outward— these are your rocket's fins. Turn the bottle upside down and tape a cardboard nose cone to the bottom. Then use the fins to balance the bottle on the blocks so that it's off the ground and you can attach the pump connector to the valve in the cork.

TESTING

You need be sure to set this up in the middle of the yard and pointing away from any sheds, buildings, vehicles, potted plants, trees, and so on—the bottle rocket launches at speed and you don't want it colliding with anything. Get people to stand back at least 3 yards (2.7m) and warn them that there will be backsplash from the water in the bottle. Make sure the cork is firmly in place in the bottle's neck and your rocket is standing upright and securely in position on the blocks. You're ready for takeoff.

Begin pumping air into the bottle. You don't need to use a lot of force—pump gently. Can you see anything happening? If you notice water escaping from the bottle's neck, you may want to add some more tape to the cork, to ensure the bottle is well sealed. Keep pumping until your rocket launches.

Once you've got the launch working neatly, try varying the amount of water in the bottle. What difference does using more or less water make to the success of takeoff and flight distance? What happens if you use a 20fl oz (590ml) bottle instead of a 68fl oz (2l) one?

ADDITIONAL SETUP

If you're launching the rocket from a grassy area or piece of earth, one neat idea for a launcher is to dig a spade or fork into the ground at an acute angle, around 20 or 30 degrees. Then you can balance the bottle in the handle a little way off the ground and have easy access to connect the pump. See what difference it makes when the bottle takes off at this angle.

You can use a ball pump adapter, the kind you use to pump up sports balls, in place of the bicycle inner-tube valve. Just push the adapter through the center of the cork and connect it to the pump in the same way.

IN CONCLUSION

This explosive experiment demonstrates English mathematician and physicist Isaac Newton's third law of motion, which he published in 1686: for every action, there is an equal and opposite reaction. As you pump air into the bottle, the pressure inside builds. This air pressure tries to push the water out of the bottle. At first, the friction between the cork and the bottle neck is enough to resist the pressure. But as you keep pumping, the pressure becomes high enough to force the cork and water out downward, and the bottle flies upward. In Newton's terms, the water and cork being pushed out downward is the action, which causes an opposite reaction: the bottle flying upward. The "action" and "opposite reaction" are equal in size, so you might expect the water and cork to travel the same distance as the plastic bottle. However, the thin plastic soda bottle flies off very quickly because it is much lighter than the water and cork.

Space rockets take off using the same principle. In their case, extremely powerful engines thrust hot air downward. This force produces an opposite reaction that drives the rocket soaring upward, away from the Earth.

ROCKET PROPULSION

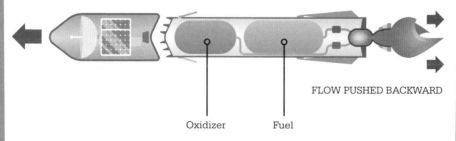

ENGINE PUSHED FORWARD

FLOW PUSHED BACKWARD

Oxidizer   Fuel

PUZZLER!?!

What did Isaac Newton discover in 1666, 20 years before his laws of motion?

#5

EXPLODING BAG

The bag that delivers a big bang!

YOU WILL NEED:
- Baking soda • Vinegar
- Small sealable freezer bag • Two paper towels

OPTIONAL:
- Sealable freezer bags of different sizes
- Warm water

!

Always take a few steps back before the "bag bomb" goes off.

SETUP

This experiment will make a mess, so be sure to set it up in an area of the backyard that you can easily clean up—and well away from anything you don't want to get messy. Prop up the bag and pour in ½ cup (118ml) of vinegar. Lay out two paper towels and pour one tablespoon of baking soda on top, in a little pile in the middle, then twist or fold the paper towels around it to make a tiny parcel. This delays the reaction for a few moments when you add the baking soda.

TESTING

Pop the paper parcel into the bag and seal it shut. Shake the bag a couple of times then place it on the ground and quickly step out of the way. Don't hang around—the reaction is fast! What happens?

Try varying the amounts of vinegar and baking soda or adding warm water to the vinegar before you add the baking soda. You can also use larger and smaller sealable freezer bags to see which one works best.

IN CONCLUSION

That went off with a bang! Could you see the reaction taking place? The interaction of the vinegar and baking soda that makes the bag pop is a classic acid-base chemical reaction, in which the acid and a base are both neutralized, leaving behind a salt (any compound formed by the neutralization of an acid by a base) and water. Vinegar is the acid—it contains acetic acid—and baking soda is the base, also known by its scientific name sodium bicarbonate. Hydrogen ions in the vinegar react with sodium and bicarbonate to form carbonic acid and sodium acetate (the salt), and the carbonic acid almost instantaneously decomposes into carbon dioxide and water. This carbon dioxide is the gas that fills the bag, increasing the pressure inside until the sealed bag pops with a bang.

You rely on the acid-base reaction in the kitchen when you use baking soda while making a cake or quick bread. The baking soda (base) is usually combined with an acidic ingredient such as buttermilk or lemon juice, and the carbon dioxide given off by the reaction causes the mixture to rise.

GIANT'S TOOTHPASTE

Set off an explosion of foamy paste

YOU WILL NEED:
- 34fl oz (1l) empty plastic soda bottle • Rubber gloves
- Measuring cup/jug • 6 percent (20 vol.) hydrogen peroxide
- Dry yeast • Food dye • Dish soap • Warm water • Funnel
- Two jugs • Spoon

OPTIONAL:
- Paper • Colored pens • Carved jack-o'-lantern • Small plastic container

This will get super-messy, so wear old clothes and choose a corner of the backyard that you don't mind cleaning up afterward. (You might also want to put down some plastic sheeting.) Put on your rubber gloves and measure out ½ cup (118ml) of the hydrogen peroxide, being very careful when handling it. Put one tablespoon of dry yeast into one jug and three tablespoons of warm water into the other. Place the soda bottle in your experiment area and pour the hydrogen peroxide into the bottle—be careful and use a funnel so you don't spill any on your clothes. Add around 6–8 drops of food dye and a squirt of dish soap. Lift the bottle and swirl the ingredients lightly to mix them. If you want to go all out, you could make a paper sleeve for your bottle saying something like "Fee, Fi, Fo, Fum Brand Giant's Toothpaste."

TESTING

Pour the warm water onto the dry yeast and stir until the two are combined. Now you're ready to make your toothpaste. Add the yeast-and-water mixture to the soda bottle, stand back, and watch what happens. Touch the bottle—what do you notice? Does it make a difference to vary the temperature of the water you add to the yeast? How about if you add unmixed dry yeast to the hydrogen peroxide? Does adding more dish soap make a difference? How about if you use a smaller or larger bottle?

You can get 6 percent (20 vol.) hydrogen peroxide at a beauty supply store. You may also be able to get 12 percent (40 vol.), and the stronger the solution the better for this demonstration.

GIANT'S TOOTHPASTE

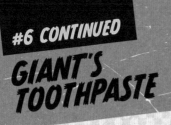

The reaction gives off oxygen, so you should be careful not to have any naked flames nearby when you start the experiment.

ADDITIONAL SETUP

A ghoulish Halloween version of this demonstration is to set up the reaction so it goes off inside a jack-o'-lantern. This will be most impressive with a large carved pumpkin—preferably with a big mouth and eyes to allow the foam to ooze out. Pour 1 cup (237ml) of hydrogen peroxide into a small plastic container inside the pumpkin (it needs to have room for the yeast mixture). Add a squirt of dish soap and a few drops of the food dye of your choice—perhaps yellow for vomit or red for blood. Mix one tablespoon of dry yeast with three tablespoons of warm water and stir them together well. Very carefully, pour the yeast solution into the hydrogen peroxide and quickly put the top of the carved pumpkin back in place. Stand back and admire your disgusting work... Yuck!

IN CONCLUSION

This impressive experiment is powered by a chemical reaction in which the hydrogen peroxide breaks down, releasing water and oxygen. The yeast works as a catalyst—an element that initiates or speeds up a chemical reaction—to speed up the decomposition of the hydrogen peroxide. The oxygen released combines with the dish soap to create the surge of foam. Did you notice that the bottle was warm on the outside? This is because the breakdown of hydrogen peroxide is an exothermic reaction: as the bonds between the hydrogen peroxide molecules break down, they release energy as heat.

Household hydrogen peroxide is a 3 percent solution, which is strong enough to kill viruses and bacteria but not powerful enough to drive this experiment—for this you need at least 6 percent (also called 20 vol.) hydrogen peroxide.

Although you have to be very careful when handling the hydrogen peroxide, the products of the experiment are nothing more dangerous than oxygen, soap, and water, so it's quite safe to pour leftover liquid down the drain and mop up the foam in your backyard using a hose or brush. Keep your gloves on, though, and don't be tempted to touch or taste the foam—there's a small chance a tiny amount of the hydrogen peroxide will not have reacted with the catalyst.

INCOMBUSTIBLE BANKNOTE

Prove you've got money to burn

YOU WILL NEED:
• Paper banknote • Barbecue tongs • Matches or a lighter • Bowl or beaker • Ethanol (or rubbing alcohol) • Water • Pinch of salt

SETUP

Make up a mixture of half ethanol, half water in the bowl or beaker—just enough to submerge the banknote in the liquid. (You can also use rubbing alcohol instead of pure ethanol, with a solution of three parts rubbing alcohol to one part water.) Add a pinch of salt to the mixture and put the banknote in the beaker. Use the barbecue tongs to move it around so that it is soaked through.

TESTING

Use the tongs to lift the banknote out of the mixture. Hold the note well in front of you and shake it lightly, allowing any excess liquid to drip off onto the ground. Now light the banknote with a match. What happens? This could be a good experiment to try at dusk or on a summer's evening, as the effect will be intensified in the half-light.

You could see if this experiment will work with other papery items: a leaf from your backyard or a page torn out of a magazine, for example. Does it matter whether the item you're going to burn is coated? How about if it's wet, as a leaf might be?

Note that some modern banknotes are polymer-based and will not work as well as older paper notes. You could try using play money from a board game.

IN CONCLUSION

It's a chemical reaction that saves your cash. When ethanol burns it reacts with oxygen and breaks down into water and carbon dioxide, giving off heat. The ethanol in the mixture you've used to soak the banknote burns but the water released by the reaction evaporates, along with the water in the original solution. This evaporation has a cooling effect and keeps the temperature below 451°F (233°C), the ignition temperature of paper. The salt you added to the mixture makes the flame burn with a yellow color, so it's easier to see. After burning for a short while, the flame goes out and your banknote is safe. It might be a little wet, though!

#8 ⚠️

PASTA ROCKET

Make a backyard version of a hybrid rocket engine

YOU WILL NEED:
• Small canning jar (without its securing collar) • Drill • Rubber gloves • 3 percent hydrogen peroxide • Active dry bread yeast • Teaspoon • Piece of tubular pasta, e.g. rigatoni or ziti • Lighter or matches • Protective eyewear

SETUP

First, drill a $\frac{1}{8}$ in (3mm) hole in the lid of the canning jar. It's important you use the jar without its securing collar. The lid must be able to blow off if the pressure inside the jar gets too high, and if you use the securing collar then the pressure might cause the jar to explode, risking injury. Set the equipment up on a table in a sheltered corner of the backyard, well away from gas outlets, naked flames, and fragile fittings. Fill the jar around three-quarters full of 3 percent hydrogen peroxide, being sure to handle it with care. (It's best to wear rubber gloves to do this.) Get your bread yeast, ziti tube, and lighter ready, and put on your protective eyewear.

TESTING

Add about one-quarter of a teaspoon (or three to four pinches) of yeast into the jar. What happens? Shake the jar lightly to mix the contents well. Do you notice any change? Place the flat top on the jar, then take the pasta tube and carefully position it over the hole drilled in the jar top. Use the lighter or matches to set the pasta tube alight and closely watch what happens to it. Where are the flames? What happens at the end of the tube? What is happening in the jar beneath? Do you notice anything if you touch the jar?

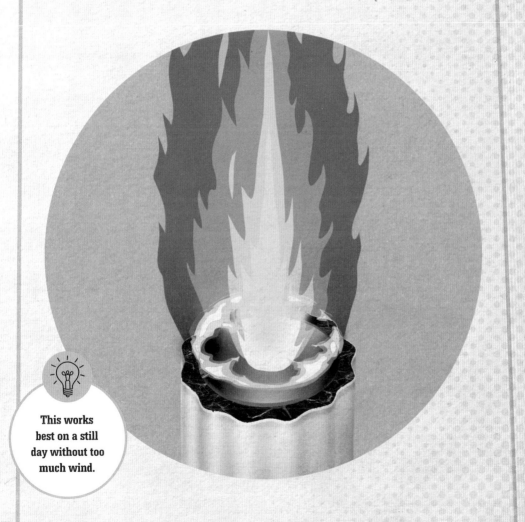

This works best on a still day without too much wind.

PASTA ROCKET

HOW ROCKET THRUST WORKS

All rocket engines work by providing downward/backward thrust that pushes the rocket upward/forward—in line with Sir Isaac Newton's third law of motion: for every action, there is an equal and opposite reaction. So, why doesn't your hybrid pasta rocket engine take off? That's because the force created by the thrust of the canning jar "engine" is pushing down into the table.

IN CONCLUSION

This really neat demonstration creates a backyard model of a hybrid rocket engine. There are three different kinds of rocket engine: solid, liquid, and hybrid. All three have a fuel and an oxidizer (usually a compound that contains oxygen) to drive the burning of the fuel. In solid rocket engines, the fuel and oxidizer are combined in a solid block; in liquid engines, the fuel and oxidizer are mixed in a liquid; whereas a hybrid engine combines a solid fuel and a liquid or gas oxidizer. Here the complex carbohydrate of the pasta tube is the solid fuel, and the reaction of the hydrogen peroxide and yeast inside the jar releases the oxygen that serves as the oxidizer.

When you add the yeast to the hydrogen peroxide in the canning jar, you'll probably see it begin bubbling away. (Sometimes you have to give it a helping hand by swirling the jar to mix up the ingredients.) The yeast contains catalase, an enzyme that serves as a catalyst for the release of oxygen from the hydrogen peroxide. This is an exothermic reaction: it releases heat. So you'll probably notice that the canning jar becomes warm as the yeast and hydrogen peroxide react with one another.

The hole in the lid of the jar funnels the oxygen up into the pasta tube you place on top. As you can see when the pasta tube is alight, the oxygen drives the burning of the fuel. You should see a powerful upward flame.

A key advantage of hybrid rocket engines is that the amount of oxidizer can be increased or reduced to control the burning of the fuel. On a more developed model of this engine there would be a valve to vary the amount of oxygen being fed to the fuel combustion. In this model your only option is to lift the lid off to remove the pasta (fuel) from the stream of oxygen (oxidizer).

Some space engineers see hybrid engines as the future. They are often cheaper to develop and easier to control than solid or liquid ones, and tend to be safer, because the fuel and oxidizer are separate—with liquid or solid engines, there is greater risk of accidental explosion.

9

POTATO GUN

Spud-zooka! Fire a root-vegetable missile!

YOU WILL NEED:
- About 18in (46cm) of thin, rigid plastic or copper piping • Metal file • Short length of bamboo cane • An uncooked potato

SETUP

Make sure the length of pipe is straight and not dented. Check the openings and make sure they're smooth all the way around. If they're not, use a small file to smooth away any roughness. Put the potato on a bench or the backyard table. Press the pipe down hard into the potato so it goes all the way through. You should now have a section of potato wedged in one end of the pipe. The pipe around your piece of potato must be completely airtight—this why you need to ensure the pipe is smooth all the way around. Repeat the process at the other end of the pipe. Your spud-zooka is now loaded and ready for action, with a potato piece in each end.

TESTING

Hold the pipe up with one end facing toward you and the other facing away, and take aim with the farthest end of the pipe. Make sure you aim away from the house and take care not to include any people or pets in your line of fire! Then take the length of cane and poke it into the potato piece in the end nearest you. What happens?

After firing, be sure to push out any potato remnants from the tube before reloading.

IN CONCLUSION

Air pressure overcomes friction to send the potato pellet at the firing end flying out of the tube toward the target. This is a great demonstration of Boyle's law, published by the scientist Robert Boyle in 1662. Boyle's law states that the relationship between the pressure and volume of a gas is inversely proportional: as one increases, the other decreases. When you plug the two ends with potato, you trap air inside the pipe. As you push the pieces of potato closer together, the volume of space the trapped air has to inhabit decreases, which, according to Boyle's law, builds the pressure in the pipe. When you first start pushing your bamboo cane through the pipe, friction between the potato piece and the inside of the pipe stops the pellet moving at the far end, but as you continue to push, the pressure increases until friction is no longer able to hold the pellet and it flies out.

The same principle is used in pressure guns deployed to launch confetti and glitter at celebrations. And you may have seen the same device used to launch compressed T-shirts into the crowd at sports or other events.

10

BIG-BANG WATERMELON

The pressure gets to this prized fruit

YOU WILL NEED:
A watermelon • Big bag of rubber bands • Old clothes • Protective eyewear (e.g. goggles, glasses, or sunglasses)

SETUP

You should wear old clothes and protective eyewear (for example, glasses) for this experiment. Take a medium-size watermelon and place it in an area of the yard where you don't mind a mess being made. Get the rubber bands ready to put on the fruit. They need to be the right size: too small and they won't go around the fruit; too large and they won't produce enough pressure. When the experiment works, it's an impressive sight, so you might want to get a friend ready to video it using their smartphone or camera.

The stretched rubber bands hold potential energy and are constantly trying to return to their original shape, and it is this potential energy that exerts a force on the watermelon and makes it explode. When you begin adding the rubber bands, they have no apparent effect: the melon's outer skin is tough and covers a thick, bendy rind, which withstands the initial pressure. As you add more and more, however, the rubber bands exert increasing pressure, finally causing a crack in the skin and rind that gradually spreads. When the skin and rind suddenly give way, the pulpy interior flies everywhere.

If you try the experiment using a larger watermelon with the same size rubber bands, you'll find the fruit will explode more quickly. This is because the more the rubber band is stretched, the greater force it exerts. Like an egg (see page 134), the watermelon is much stronger lengthwise than around its middle, and if you try adding rubber bands this way you'll need to be patient: you may need more than 500 to explode the fruit!

TESTING

All you need to do is put rubber bands around the middle of the fruit. Little by little they will increase the pressure on the watermelon. Watch out for cracks appearing in the surface of the fruit, then see what happens.

Does the size of the fruit make a difference? And does it matter which direction you put on the bands—lengthwise or around the middle of the melon?

PUZZLER!?!

How do the rubber bands get their potential energy?

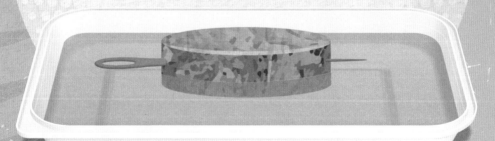

PART 2

NATURAL WONDERS

CONTENTS

#11
OOBLECK QUICKSAND

When is a liquid not a liquid?

YOU WILL NEED:
• Cornstarch • Water
• Old wading pool or large tub big enough for you to take a few steps in
• Bucket
OPTIONAL:
• Subwoofer • Plastic wrap • Bowl

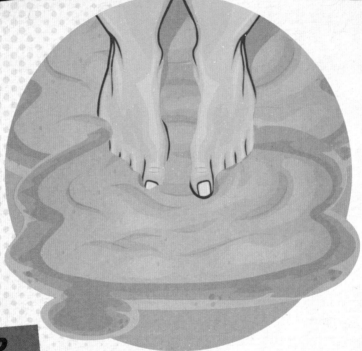

SETUP

The container you choose needs to be big enough for you to walk across and take at least three or four steps—an old wading pool or empty sandbox is ideal. Make up a mixture of two parts cornstarch to one part water in a bucket and mix it with your hands. The substance you've created is called Oobleck. Try moving your hand about loosely and scrunching your hand to make a fist. How does it feel? Pour the mixture into the container and mix up some more Oobleck—you need to make enough to fill the container to a depth of about 6–9in (15–23cm). Take off your shoes and socks, and either roll your pants up high or change into your shorts or bathing suit.

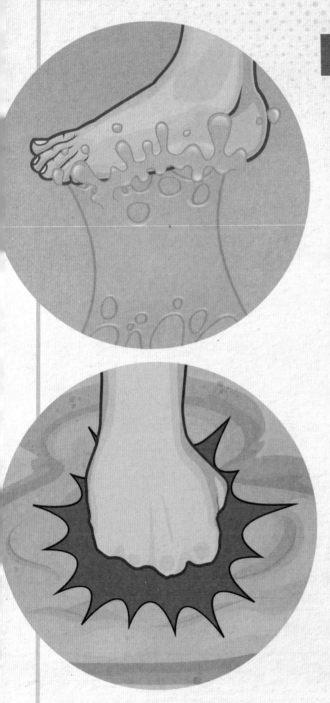

TESTING

Step into the mixture and stand still. What happens? Can you lift your foot? How about if you try running on the spot? Get out and then walk swiftly across the container. What's different? Get out again and try stamping on the mixture with one foot. If the container's large enough, try taking a short run-up and running across the mixture. Do you feel like a superhero? You can also try getting down on your hands and knees to see what happens when you punch the mixture.

!

An important warning: after you've finished the experiment, put the mixture in a few large bottles or a large trash bag and put them out with the trash. You'll block your drains—and incur a huge plumbing bill—if you try pouring it down the drain.

OOBLECK QUICKSAND

ADDITIONAL SETUP

Here's a noisy and messy Oobleck side-experiment! For this, you'll need to lay a subwoofer down on its back, so that the speaker cone faces upward, and cover the surface with plastic wrap, taping it securely in place to protect your speaker. Now make up a fresh batch of Oobleck mixture as before: 2 cups (473ml) of cornstarch to 1 cup (237ml) of water. Mix it up well in a bowl with your hands, then pour the liquid directly onto the plastic wrap. Turn on the dance music—try music with a heavy, repetitive bass beat—and pump up the volume! What happens to the Oobleck? Experiment with different tunes and sound effects you find on the Internet.

Try poking and lifting the Oobleck on the speaker with a finger or spoon to get the movement started.

IN CONCLUSION

The answer to our jokey question "When is a liquid not a liquid?" could be: when it's a non-Newtonian fluid. This is what our Oobleck is—a fluid that does not behave in line with Sir Isaac Newton's law of viscosity, which states that a liquid should have the same level of viscosity (essentially, thickness) whether it has stress (force) applied to it or not. Unlike in normal liquids, in non-Newtonian fluids, viscosity changes when force is applied. Our Oobleck is liquid but becomes solid when you apply force to it: when you walk on the quicksand or punch the surface of the liquid. The same thing happens in the dancing Oobleck demonstration: the force of the sound waves from the speaker makes the liquid solidify in patterns—you can "see" the sound waves.

If you looked at cornstarch under a microscope you'd see millions of tiny, irregularly shaped starch particles. Add water and these particles slide over one another: the mixture behaves like a liquid. Suddenly apply a force to the liquid, however, and the starch particles are driven together and the water molecules are squeezed out: the mixture behaves like a solid. When you stop walking or punching, you remove the force and the solid becomes liquid once more.

We called our experiment "Oobleck quicksand," but the Oobleck is actually more like the opposite of quicksand. It's a liquid that under some circumstances behaves as a solid, known as a shear thickening non-Newtonian fluid. Quicksand is a solid (water-saturated sand) that can behave like a liquid, known as a shear thinning non-Newtonian fluid. Ketchup is another shear thinning non-Newtonian fluid—that's why it gets runnier when you shake it.

HOW THE OOBLECK GOT ITS NAME

Oobleck takes its name from the children's book *Bartholomew and the Oobleck*, by Dr. Seuss, which was first published in 1949. In the book, the word refers to a sticky green substance that the hero has to save his kingdom from.

12

HOMEMADE TORNADO

Create a twister in a bottle

YOU WILL NEED:
- Two empty 68fl oz (2l) plastic soda bottles
- Metal washer • Glitter
- Sticky tape • Water

SETUP

Take the two soda bottles and fill one about three-quarters full of water. Add the glitter—this will make any currents in the water easier to see. Put the washer at the opening of the bottle and then turn the other bottle upside down and position it on top. Tape the two bottles securely neck to neck, so the join is airtight and watertight.

TESTING

Turn the two bottles over like an hourglass, so the empty one is underneath the one containing the water and glitter. You'll probably need to keep a hand on the top-heavy contraption to stop it from toppling over. Watch what happens. Do you hear anything? Wait for the water to flow, under pressure of gravity, into the lower bottle. Turn the bottles over once more. This time hold the bottles lightly and make a circular movement, so the water is swirling. Does anything different happen this time?

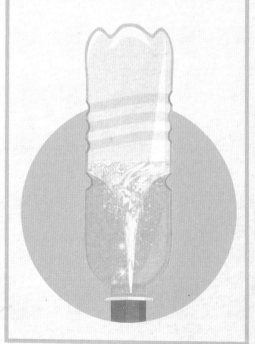

IN CONCLUSION

When you set the water in the top bottle swirling you create a vortex— a spiraling movement of liquids and gases around an empty center. You probably see a vortex every day when you watch water spinning around the drain in a sink or bathtub. In this experiment the vortex makes it easier for water in the top bottle to exchange with air in the lower one; as the water passes down, air rises to replace it. The vortex creates the tornado effect you see in the water. When the two bottles are stationary, there is no vortex and either water flows down or air rises up— creating the "glug, glug" you probably heard as the water and air took turns to exchange.

The word "tornado" usually refers to a fast-rotating air column between a cloud and the earth during a powerful storm. A tornado develops when winds blowing in opposite directions create a horizontal vortex that is then tipped to the vertical by warmed air rising up from the ground.

PUZZLER!?!

True or false: Water always spins clockwise in the vortex around the drain in the northern hemisphere.

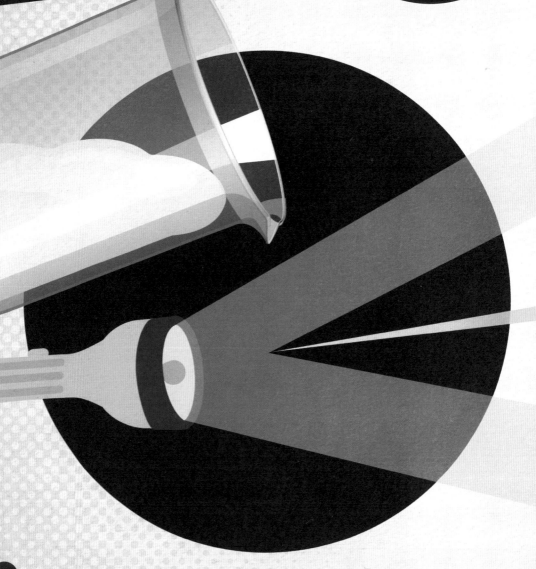

#13

GAS TRICKS

You can't see carbon dioxide gas—or can you?

SETUP

This demonstration needs darkness, so it's best to do it on a dark night in a corner of the backyard away from any artificial lighting. You can either set everything up in the daytime before it gets dark or use a camping lamp to help you see what you're doing.

You can also try this experiment in the daytime on a sunny day. Use a glass jug or a jar and hold it up to a sunlit white wall or, if you have a backyard shed, hold it up to sunlight streaming in through the window. You can also observe a similar effect inside the jug itself. Hold it up to the sunlight and look at what happens to the light as it passes through.

Put your materials on the backyard table and put two tablespoons of baking soda in the jug. Set up a white background nearby—a white screen, a section of white wall, or a large sheet of white paper will do. You'll need a helper for the demonstration, to shine the flashlight while you hold the jug up against the white background.

TESTING

Slowly pour vinegar into the jug. The exact amount doesn't matter; just make sure you leave space at the top so the jug is only around half full. The baking soda will instantly start foaming. Allow the jug to fill up with this foam and then wait a few seconds until the foaming has died down a little. Now, turn any other lights off and the flashlight on. Hold the jug up against the white background while your helper shines the light directly at it. Imagine that the jug is full of liquid and tilt it slightly, as if you're pouring the liquid out very gently. Look at the light on the white background. What do you see? What do you think is causing this effect?

GAS TRICKS

You could try varying the amounts of vinegar and baking soda you use, to see what difference it makes to how quickly and how much the balloons inflate.

ADDITIONAL SETUP

You can also test the power of the baking soda/vinegar reaction with a balloon. First blow up and deflate the balloon so that it has more give. Now take an empty 20fl oz (590ml) soda bottle and pour around ¼ cup (60ml) of vinegar in the bottom. Use a funnel to put two teaspoons of baking soda inside the balloon. (If you don't have a funnel you can ask an assistant to help by holding the neck of the balloon open.) Wrap the mouth of the balloon around the top of the bottle, positioning it so that the main part of the balloon flops down over the outside of the bottle. Holding the balloon tightly in place, lift the main part of the balloon up vertically, so the baking soda falls down into the bottle. What do you see inside the bottle and what happens to the balloon?

IN CONCLUSION

The reaction between vinegar (acetic acid) and baking soda produces carbonic acid. This is extremely unstable and immediately breaks down into water and carbon dioxide. As carbon dioxide is heavier—that is, denser—than oxygen, in the first experiment it pushes all the oxygen out of the jar and sinks down to lower areas, so the carbon dioxide stays in the jar after the foaming has stopped. When you tilt the jar you direct the carbon dioxide downward and it pours out, just as a liquid would. Did you see shadows and shimmers of light against the white background? The light from the flashlight (or sunlight, if you try the demo in the daytime) is bent when it hits the stream of carbon dioxide gas. The light travels more slowly through carbon dioxide gas than through air. As a result, the light is concentrated in some sections and there are shadows in other areas. You're making the carbon dioxide—a colorless, odorless, and otherwise invisible gas—briefly visible.

In the experiment with the balloon, the carbon dioxide gas produced in the reaction fills the bottle and tries to leave. Because the balloon is attached to the top, the gas has nowhere to go, so it pushes against the balloon and inflates it.

SLICED ICE

Split ice then watch it seal itself

YOU WILL NEED:
• Large ice cube • Ruler
• Building brick or something similarly heavy • Wire (e.g. fishing wire or guitar string)
• Polystyrene block from packaging • Two weights— 68fl oz (2l) water bottles filled with water are ideal

SETUP

Take the largest ice cube you can find in your freezer. Tie your two weights to each end of the wire. Place the ruler so that it's sticking out over the edge of your patio table and put a brick or other heavy object on the other end to secure it in position. Place the ice on top of the polystyrene and sit that on top the ruler. Then lay the wire across the ice and watch what happens.

IN CONCLUSION

The pressure of the wire—created by the weights pulling down—melts the ice beneath it. But as the wire passes through the ice, the pressure above is less than the pressure below and the ice refreezes. This phenomenon is called regelation, and it's the reason the block remains intact rather than falling into two pieces. Once the wire has traveled all the way through the ice cube, you can pick it up and see the track made by the wire.

The fact that pressure melts ice is what makes ice skating possible. The pressure of the skate melts the ice immediately beneath it and the skater zips along on a thin layer of water. So give thanks to science next time you're speeding across the ice, readying yourself to do a Russian split jump!

This experiment is probably one for a winter's day. In very hot weather the ice will melt pretty quickly.

TESTING

Pulled down by the weights, the wire cuts through the ice. How long does it take to start slicing through and how long does it take to cut right through? Once the wire has passed through the ice, does the block fall into two pieces?

You could try experimenting with ice cubes of different thicknesses. Does it matter what kind of wire you use? What if you use much smaller weights?

MAKE YOUR OWN BLACK HOLE

See how black holes work— using a piece of fruit

YOU WILL NEED:
- Piece of stretchy fabric (e.g. Spandex) • Two ping-pong balls • Apple or orange • Two helpers

OPTIONAL:
- Ruler • Marker pen

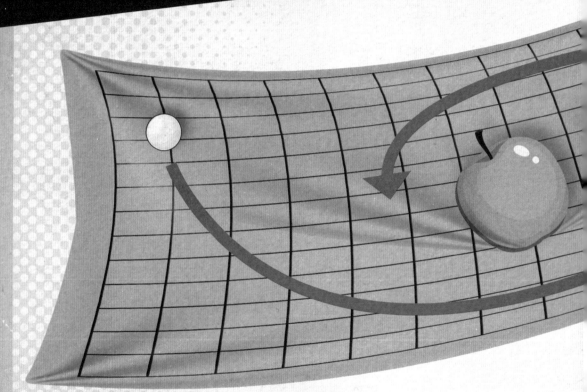

SETUP

Ask your assistants to hold the stretchy fabric between them so that it's taut. Place the ping-pong balls and the apple or orange nearby, so that they're within reach.

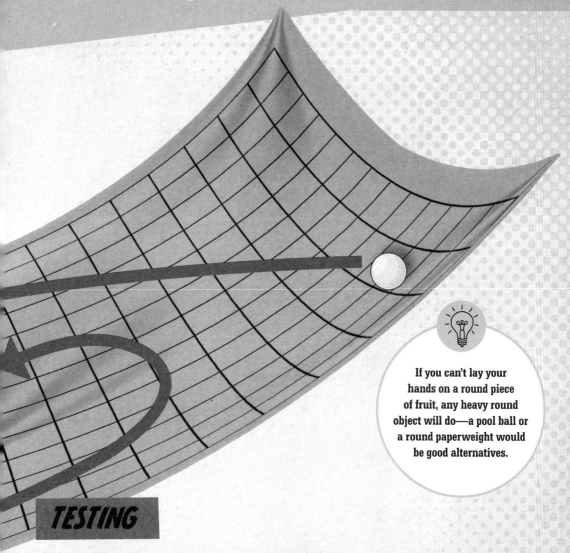

If you can't lay your hands on a round piece of fruit, any heavy round object will do—a pool ball or a round paperweight would be good alternatives.

TESTING

Place one of the ping-pong balls on the fabric and see what happens. Next, try rolling one of the ping-pong balls across the taut fabric. What shape is the path it follows? Try rolling both balls across the fabric and note what you see.

Next, put the apple or heavy ball in the middle of the taut fabric. If you release the ping-pong ball at the edge of the fabric what happens to it? And what happens if you try to roll the ping-pong ball across the fabric?

Try doing it at different speeds—does it make a difference? Then check out what happens when you roll two ping-pong balls at once.

Put the balls and apple aside and lay the fabric on a flat surface. Taking the ruler and marker pen, draw a regular grid onto the fabric. Its lines should cross one another at right angles. Now repeat the tests and watch what happens to the shapes of the grid squares.

MAKE YOUR OWN BLACK HOLE

IN CONCLUSION

The experiment is a really neat demonstration of how gravity works according to Albert Einstein's theory of general relativity. The dip in the fabric caused by the weight of the apple works like a black hole in space. In a black hole, gravity is so strong that everything nearby is sucked in, including light. Here, nothing can roll across the fabric close to our "hole" without falling into it.

In classical physics—called "Newtonian," after English mathematician Sir Isaac Newton—gravity is a force of attraction between two objects. All objects have a gravitational attraction toward one another, but we only feel it if the object's mass (the amount of matter it contains) is very large: gravity doesn't pull you toward your best friend because they don't have enough mass, but it does pull you toward the Earth because it has a huge mass (5.972×10^{24}kg).

According to Einstein, space and time are a four-dimensional continuum that he called "spacetime," and gravity works when objects of very large mass cause spacetime to curve. A human body causes a very small curve in spacetime, the Earth causes a much larger one.

Black holes are spots in space with such a large mass that they create an immensely strong gravitational force.

The force is so strong that nothing—not even light—can escape, and so astronomers cannot see black holes, but they can tell they exist by the effect the holes have on nearby objects. For example, black holes affect the orbit of nearby stars. In an area around the black hole, which astronomers call the "event horizon," everything gets sucked in. The size of the event horizon depends on the mass (the power) of the black hole.

Place a ping-pong ball on the taut fabric and it sits still. Roll it across the taut fabric and it will travel in a straight line.

HOW DOES A BLACK HOLE FORM?

Scientists say black holes are created when massive stars run out of fuel and cannot support their gaseous outer regions. They collapse inward, forming a more and more concentrated mass. Eventually, this mass is infinite, concentrated in a single point. This is called a singularity and a black hole results.

Roll two ping-pong balls across the material and they are not particularly affected by one another. But when you drop your apple or pool ball in the center of the fabric, you create a dip that is the equivalent of a black hole. Roll your ping-pong ball across the fabric now and it is likely to roll down into the dip—just as a passing object will be sucked into a black hole. The faster you roll the ball, the more likely it will escape the attraction of the hole. If you roll it right along the edge of the fabric, it will likely go in a straight line—it is outside the "event horizon" of your homemade black hole.

#16
FLOATING COMPASS

Use the Earth's magnetic field to find your way

SETUP

Lost in the woods and need to find your way? Maybe your smartphone died and you're not sure where you are? This small kit provides a neat backup to a conventional compass for finding magnetic north.

Hold the needle and run the magnet along its length, from the eye to the point, around 30 times. This magnetizes the needle. Next, carefully push the needle lengthwise through the center of the cork.

TESTING

Pour a little water from a bottle, or scooped up from a pond, puddle, or stream, into the plastic container and float the cork in the water. The point of the needle will point toward magnetic north. You've created a floating compass!

In fact, all you really need for this experiment is the magnet and the needle. How else could you float the magnetized needle? How about trying it using a dry leaf in a pond or puddle—just balance the needle on top of the leaf.

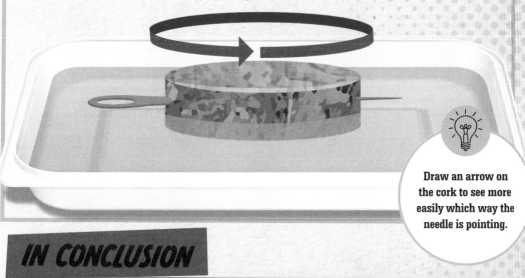

Draw an arrow on the cork to see more easily which way the needle is pointing.

IN CONCLUSION

The Earth's magnetic field (the geomagnetic field), which wraps around the entire planet, pulls the magnetized needle to align north–south. This magnetic field is mostly generated in the Earth's core and, like a simple bar magnet—and the magnetized needle—it has two poles: north and south. But magnetic north and south are not the same as the geographic North and South Poles, which lie on the Earth's axis. There's a difference of around 11 degrees between magnetic north and geographic north.

We know that opposite charges attract. So why should the magnet's north pole be attracted to Earth's magnetic north, and not the other way around? This is because the magnetic north and south poles are actually named incorrectly. They were named after the poles of the compass before the magnetic field was fully understood.

17

CLOUD MAKER

Create your own weather

YOU WILL NEED:
• Empty 68fl oz (2l) plastic bottle • Water
• Matches

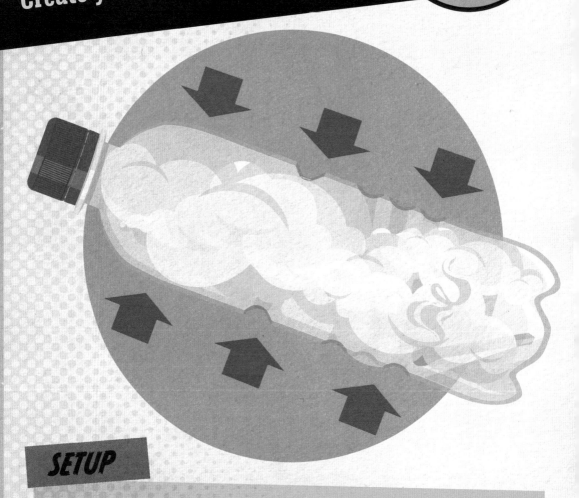

SETUP

Take the water bottle and pour a little water into the bottom. You could scoop up a little from a birdbath or pond, if you have one, or pour some from a backyard tap. Put the bottle on a table or the ground, with the lid off.

TESTING

Light a match, blow out the flame, and hold the match, still smoking, just inside the bottle. Once a little smoke has collected inside, drop the match into the bottle. Screw the cap on tightly and squeeze the bottle really hard for about 15 seconds while shaking it gently with a circular motion—just enough to make the liquid in the bottom swirl around. Then put the bottle down. What happens when you let go and the bottle expands again?

Repeat the process: squeeze and swirl, then let go. Try heating up the water a little before you put it into the bottle. How does that change what you see?

PUZZLER!?!

True or false: Fog and mist form in the same way as clouds.

IN CONCLUSION

The sealed bottle contains water and air molecules as well as smoke particles from the match. When you squeeze the bottle, you increase the pressure within it. This causes the water molecules to heat up and some of them evaporate. Then, when you let go of the bottle, the pressure, and so the temperature, falls: the water vapor molecules condense as water droplets on the particles of smoke. This is what creates the cloud.

The experiment recreates very closely how clouds form in the Earth's atmosphere. The heat of the sun causes surface water to evaporate from rivers, lakes, and seas. The water vapor naturally rises to where the atmospheric pressure and air temperature are lower, and its molecules then condense as droplets of water. They attach themselves to pollen dust or pollution particles, forming a cloud, just as the water molecules in the bottle attached to the smoke particles. The drops increase in size until they are big enough to fall as rain—or snow and hail when it's very cold.

18

COLOR-CHANGING FLOWERS

Turn white petals pink—and blue, and orange, and green...

SETUP

Select three or four different colors of food dye and place them on the backyard table with the same number of glass jars (or you can use small vases). Cut some white flowers from the backyard—enough to put one or two in each of the jars. (If you don't have flowers growing, you can pick some up from a florist or supermarket.) White carnations and roses are perfect for this demonstration, and chrysanthemums or oxeye daisies will work well, too. Half fill each jar with water, then add around 15 drops of food dye to each jar, using a different color for each, and mix well. Cut the flower stems with a knife at an angle of 45 degrees, so the stalks are around 5in (13cm) long. Put one or two flowers in each jar and leave them for a few hours—keep an eye on your flowers to see what happens.

TESTING

Do you notice anything after a few minutes? How about after an hour? And two hours? You could take photos every 15 minutes or so, so that you can document the change that takes place. Look again after three and four hours.

What happens if you move one of the flowers from one jar to another? You can also try mixing two or more colors of food dye in one jar of water, and seeing what effect that has on the flowers.

This makes a great demonstration for a backyard barbecue on a summer's day—you and your guests will see intriguing results over the course of an afternoon.

IN CONCLUSION

The flowers will take on the hue of the colored water in which they are placed. You may see some color change after 10 minutes or so—certainly within an hour. Look at the stems and any branching leaves as well as the petals.

The flowers draw up water from the jar by capillary action. The water molecules are attracted to the molecules on the sides of the narrow flower stem (adhesion) and are also bound together by surface tension and cohesion. This combination is strong enough for water to be pulled up the plant stem against gravity. Water normally evaporates from the stem, leaves, and petals (transpiration), and more water is sucked up. The dye in the food coloring does not evaporate, however, so the petals and stem take on the color. If you leave a flower for two to three hours in one jar and then move it to another, both colors will dye the petals. You may find that if you mix colors in the water, they will separate out in the flower petals.

19

RAINBOW SHOW

Unleash the colors in everyday sunlight

YOU WILL NEED:
• Hose (or mist spray bottle) • Glass of water • Glass prism • Piece of white paper or cardstock
OPTIONAL
• Spray gun or nozzle

SETUP

You should wait until the sun is shining brightly to do this experiment. (It's ideal for a hot day, when people won't mind drying off naturally if they are "accidentally" sprayed with water.) Set your hose spray gun or nozzle to the mist setting. (If your hose doesn't have a spray gun or nozzle that you can control, you can try putting your thumb over the top of the pipe to create a fine spray.) Put a glass of water on the backyard table with a piece of white paper or cardstock propped up behind it. Sit the glass prism on the table, next to the glass.

TESTING

With the sun behind you, spray the water across the backyard. What do you see? Look for colors in the mist as the sunlight hits it. Now look at the light falling through the glass of water onto the white paper or cardstock. What do you see here? Can you get the same results with the prism? You may have to adjust the spray, move the glass of water, or shift the prism to get a good display of rainbow colors.

IN CONCLUSION

We see sunlight as white light, but sunlight actually contains all the colors of the rainbow: red, orange, yellow, green, blue, indigo, and violet. When sunlight hits water droplets in the mist (or molecules of glass in the drinking glass or prism) at an angle, it bends. Different colors of light travel at different speeds and so will bend, or refract, at different angles. The difference in these angles causes the white light to spread out into all the colors of the rainbow.

The water-spray rainbow is created by the same process that occurs when you see a rainbow in the sky. Sunlight hits water molecules in the atmosphere and spreads out into all the colors of the rainbow, but in fact we only see one color from each raindrop; it's all the raindrops working together that creates the rainbow we see. This is why rainbows occur when the sun comes out while it is raining or right after a storm.

PUZZLER!?!

Can you think of any other ways to make a rainbow from sunlight?

20

HOMEMADE LIGHTNING

Create your own summer storm

YOU WILL NEED:
• Styrofoam™ tray • Styrofoam™ cup • Aluminum pie tray
• Sticky tape or putty adhesive
• Wooden or glass table

OPTIONAL:
• Wool sweater or scarf
• Balloon • Metal spoon

The darker it is the better for this demonstration. Choose an overcast night when there's little natural light and find the darkest spot in your backyard, away from any streetlights or other light sources.

SETUP

Take the Styrofoam™ cup and stick it securely with the putty adhesive or tape to the center of the aluminum pie tray. This needs to be secure enough to use as a handle to lift the pie tray later on.

TESTING

Rub the Styrofoam™ tray vigorously against the hair on your head for two to three minutes. (If you don't want to mess up your hair, you can rub it against a wool sweater or scarf instead.) Then put the Styrofoam™ tray down on a glass or wooden surface, such as a backyard table—don't use your table if it's made of metal. If you don't have a glass or wooden table, you could put the tray on the ground. Gently pick up the aluminum pie tray by the Styrofoam™ cup and drop it onto the Styrofoam™ tray. Now touch the edge of the pie tin with your forefinger.

Watch closely—what happens? Try lifting the pie tin with the handle and using your other hand to touch the pie tin again. And again, and again…

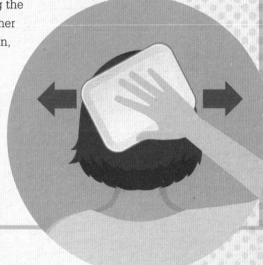

Another even simpler version of this demonstration uses a balloon and a metal spoon. Blow up the balloon and rub it against your hair or a wool sweater, then touch the metal spoon to the balloon. Do you see anything?

IN CONCLUSION

The spark you see—like a lightning bolt in the sky—is caused by static electricity being suddenly discharged. When you rub the Styrofoam™ against your hair or the sweater, negatively charged particles (electrons) build up on the surface of the Styrofoam™—it gains a static electric charge. In metals, some electrons are called free electrons because they can move about inside the material. When you place the aluminum pie tin on the Styrofoam™ tray, the free electrons in the tin, which also have a negative charge, are repelled by the negative charge of the tray. (Opposite charges attract, but identical charges repel one another.) The free electrons all gather at the edge of the tin, and when you touch the edge, the electrons jump to your finger, causing a spark as they travel through the air. It's a mini lightning bolt!

PART 3

SPLASH

CONTENTS

21

NO-POUR GLASS

YOU WILL NEED:
• Drinking glass
• Water
• Cardstock
OPTIONAL:
• Dish soap

Watch water defy gravity

Gather a few friends ready to be amazed as you defy the laws of nature.

SETUP

You may have some spillages while you're getting to grips with this demonstration, so set this up in an area of the backyard where you don't mind making a splash. Start by filling your glass completely with water—it's important that it's full to the brim—then put the cardstock over the top of the glass.

TESTING

Pick up the glass and, holding the cardstock in position, carefully turn it upside down, supporting it from underneath. It's best to hold the glass away from your body—just in case. Now remove the hand that's holding the card in place. What do you expect to happen? What actually happens?

You can try the experiment again, but this time wipe a little dish soap around the rim of the glass before you fill it and put the card in position. Then invert it as before. What happens now?

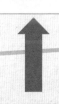

IN CONCLUSION

Atmospheric air pressure is constantly pushing around us in all directions. In this demonstration the atmospheric pressure is pushing upward on the card from below. There is a small amount of air trapped in the glass when we invert it and this creates a pocket of low pressure. The atmospheric pressure outside the glass is much larger due to all the air molecules colliding with the card. The smaller air pressure in the glass combines with gravity to push down on the card, and the external air pressure pushes up against the card. These forces equal one another so the card stays in position. What's more, the water molecules adhere (are attracted) to one another, creating surface tension. They are also attracted to the molecules in the paper (cohesion). These forces, working together, hold the card in place, preventing the water from pushing it downward.

If you tried the experiment with dish soap on the glass rim, you'll have found that it didn't work. This is because the soap breaks the surface tension and allows the water to spill out.

#22

NO CORKSCREW? NO PROBLEM!

Open your wine bottle with a shoe

YOU WILL NEED:
- Full bottle of wine
- Flat-soled shoe
- A wall

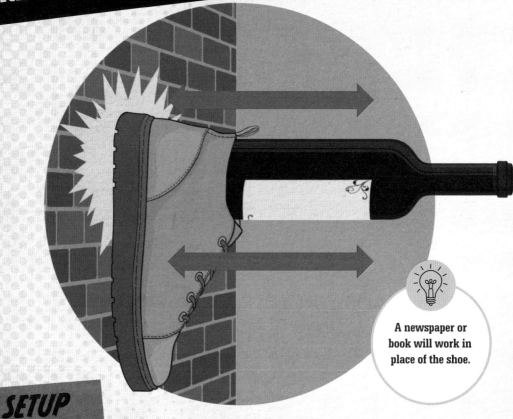

A newspaper or book will work in place of the shoe.

SETUP

It's Saturday evening and you've lost your corkscrew, but you'd like to open that bottle of Merlot. Frustrating? Not necessarily. Use this makeshift method to open your bottle.

First, take any foil off the bottle top. Standing up, take a flat-soled shoe (avoid cushioned sneakers) and hold it against one of the walls in your backyard. Hold the bottle in the other hand and place it inside the shoe, so that its base sits facing the wall.

TESTING

Holding the bottle and shoe together, hit the sole of the shoe against the wall, making sure you hit with the bottle's base parallel to the brickwork. (It's vital not to hit the bottle at an angle otherwise it could shatter.) Don't be too hesitant—you need to use force—but don't hit too hard. What's happening to the wine inside the bottle? Do you see a difference in its appearance? Do you hear a noise at the cork end? Does it matter if it's a new, plastic cork rather than a traditional one?

IN CONCLUSION

When you hit the shoe against the wall, the impact between the shoe and the wall generates a force that travels down the length of the bottle toward the cork. The wine transmits this force very efficiently from the base of the bottle to the neck because the liquid fills the bottle completely and so cannot slosh around, meaning the wine molecules behave as if they were part of a solid. Each time you hit the bottle against the shoe you're effectively driving the cork outward from inside the bottle. This process creates very small bubbles, which is why you might notice your wine looking a little cloudy. Eventually, the cork will move out far enough for you to be able to grab hold of it with your fingers and pull it out. Now all you need to do is find a glass and a friend to share the bottle—cheers!

CRAZY SAND

Water can't wet this sand

SETUP

Divide your sand in two and spread one half in a thin layer on the baking sheet. Put the other half aside. Take the fabric protector and spray the tray of sand evenly all over until it looks wet. Set this aside to dry in a well-ventilated area. Once it's dry, mix up the sprayed sand by hand, then spray it a second time and leave it to dry again. You want the sand to be well coated for the experiment to work.

TESTING

Fill both glass jars around two-thirds full of water. Gently pour the sprayed sand in a continuous stream into one jar and then pour a stream of unsprayed sand into the other. Compare the appearance of the sand in each jar. Put a hand into each jar and pick up some of the sand. What does it look like when you lift it from the water and drop it back in? How is it different in the two cases? Now take the jar containing water and the sprayed sand and gently pour the water off into one of the bowls. What's left in the bottom of the jar? Can you pour it back onto the baking sheet?

Empty and dry the bowl you used. Pour some of the sprayed sand into one bowl and some of the unsprayed sand into the other. Take the pipette (the dispensing top of a bottle of eye or ear drops works just as well), pick up a few drops of water, and drop them onto the sand in each bowl. Why does the water look so different on the two types of sand?

Fill one of the jars about two-thirds full of water once more. Hold a spoon at an angle underwater and gently pour sprayed sand onto it. What does it look like? What happens when you lift the spoon vertically up out of the water?

You have to leave the tray of sprayed sand to dry in a well-ventilated area, so this experiment is best done outside on a warm, dry day.

You can buy ready-made "magic sand" in toyshops or online.

IN CONCLUSION

We know from building sandcastles at the beach that soft, dry sand collapses into a pile, but when mixed with water, the same sand can be used to build solid sandcastle walls. Yet something completely different happened when we mixed the sprayed sand with water in this demonstration, right?

You probably found that if you poured a small amount of sprayed sand very lightly into the water most of it stayed on the surface, but when you poured a steady stream most of it sank, clumping into columns and beads and other weird and wonderful shapes. Then, when you poured the water off once more, the same sand was dry again. When you gently delivered drops of water onto the treated sand with the pipette, you likely found that the water did not sink in, but sat on the surface in beads and globules.

This crazy sand demonstrates the difference between hydrophobic (water-hating) and hydrophilic (water-loving) substances. Normal sand is a hydrophilic substance: the water molecules adhere to the grains of sand and the water molecules cohere or stick to one another, forming connections between the grains that make the wet sand clump together, so it is malleable. Once the sand and water are mixed, it's not easy to separate them again, except by evaporation through sunlight or another heat source.

By spraying the sand with a water-repellent spray, you coated the grains with an oily film. Oil is hydrophobic—it will not mix with water—and the spray makes the sand hydrophobic, too. So, when you poured the sand into the water, the coated sand molecules stuck together rather than mixing with the water molecules—they either stayed on the surface of the water or formed columns and blobs underwater. They formed these shapes to make the surface contact between the water and the sand as small as possible. Then, when you poured the water off, the sand was as dry as it had been at the start.

THE MAGIC OF SAND

Our crazy sand is a homemade version of commercially available "magic sand." This material was originally used to treat oil spills in the ocean. The magic sand was sprinkled on the ocean surface, where it would combine with the oil particles. Once enough oil and sand had combined, it became heavy enough to sink to the ocean floor. This method of oil capture was discontinued, however, because magic sand is too expensive for large-scale use and there was concern that the method might have adverse environmental effects.

Magic sand has also been used in very cold regions, such as the Arctic. Because it expels water, it does not freeze, so it can be packed around electrical and telephone wiring elements underground.

#24
BOUNCING BUBBLES

Did you know you could bounce bubbles in your hand?

YOU WILL NEED:
- Water • Dish soap
- Bubble wand
- Clean wool gloves or other wool clothing, e.g. a scarf • Glycerin or corn syrup

Make the bubble mixture the night before you want to use it.

SETUP

It's best to do this experiment on a still day. Make up a mixture of three parts water to one part dish soap. Stir them together gently so as to mix them well but without making bubbles in the mixture. Get your wool gloves ready, or find a wool scarf or sweater. If you get together a few people all wearing wool gloves, it's fun to play with the amazing bouncing bubbles together.

TESTING

Take the bubble wand, dip it into the mixture, and blow some bubbles. Try to bounce the bubbles off your bare hands. What happens? Put on the gloves or wrap one of your hands in another woolen item. Now blow some more bubbles and try to bounce these off your hands. What happens? Why do you think there's a difference? How long do the bubbles last?

Try adding more dish soap to the mixture and repeating the experiment. Then add a few drops of glycerin or corn syrup to the bubble mixture. Does this make a difference to the bubbles and how quickly they pop? You can experiment with different bubble mixtures containing more or less glycerin.

IN CONCLUSION

You probably found that mixing dish soap and water allowed you to blow lots of large bubbles and that adding a few drops of glycerin or corn syrup meant the bubbles you made were stronger and lasted longer—but why?

Surface tension prevents large bubbles from forming in normal water. Dish soap reduces the water's surface tension. The bubbles consist of a thin layer of water molecules sandwiched between two layers of detergent molecules. In time, the water evaporates and the bubbles burst. The glycerin or corn syrup forms bonds with the water molecules and slows evaporation, meaning the bubbles last longer.

Bubbles pop when they encounter dirt or oil, so when you tried bouncing bubbles off your bare hands you probably found they burst almost immediately. When you wear wool gloves, the bubble will bounce because the wool provides a surface that's free of dirt and oil. After a while, though, gravity will make bubbles pop. It pulls the bubble mixture downward and the area on top gets thinner and thinner until it gives way—the bubble disintegrates.

SWIM-CAP SLAP

How scientists put their cap on

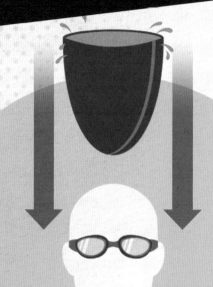

This experiment is probably one for a warm day!

SETUP

You're going to get wet during this demonstration, so it's best to wear a bathing suit or old clothes. If you have a swimming pool in your backyard, you could sit on the edge, otherwise you can just sit on a patio chair. Turn the swim cap inside out and fill it with water.

Get your helper to hold the water-filled cap about 2ft (0.6m) above your head. Prepare yourself, then ask them to drop the cap vertically onto your head. What happens?

IN CONCLUSION

It is the force of gravity, combined with the low viscosity of water and its remarkable surface tension, that makes this demonstration work. Once you or your friend have released the water-filled cap, gravity causes it to accelerate downward at a speed of 32ft per second (9.8m per second). When it hits your head, the water's surface tension and low viscosity cause it to flow down around your skull, and this has the effect of wrapping the cap around your head.

A high surface tension means that the water molecules are strongly attracted to one another and hold together. Water's low viscosity means it flows quickly and easily. Scientists also describe low-viscosity liquids (like water) as thin and high-viscosity liquids (like syrup) as thick. Imagine a swim cap filled with syrup dropped on your head—the syrup would run slowly, dripping out. With this demonstration, the easy, gravity-driven flow of water turns the cap inside out around your head. So you may be a bit wet, but your cap's on. Look, mom, no hands!

WATER ZOOM

YOU WILL NEED:
- Two large bowls
- Two pipettes • Water
- 20–30 small matchsticks • Sheet of paper • Scissors
- Dish soap

Break the tension— the surface tension

If you don't have any small matchsticks you can try the experiment with other small, lightweight objects, such as paper confetti, or a few petals or dried leaves from your backyard.

SETUP

Place the bowls on the backyard table and fill them both with water. Gather together 20–30 matchsticks—it doesn't matter whether they are used or not—and divide them into two groups. Finally, cut out two small boat shapes from the paper.

TESTING

First set the two groups of matchsticks floating in the two bowls. Take the two pipettes (the top of a bottle of eye or ear drops will work just as well); pick up a little water in one pipette and a little dish soap in the other. Squeeze a few drops of water into one bowl and a few drops of dish soap into the other. What happens? Can you think why the two sets of matchsticks might behave so differently?

Now empty the bowls out and fill one back up with clean water. Place the two paper boats on the surface. If you have a helper, it's fun to do the next part with two people racing the boats. Get one person to use the pipette to release a drop of water behind one boat and the second to release a drop of dish soap behind the other. Who wins?

IN CONCLUSION

These results are all due to the surface tension of water. Water molecules are strongly attracted to one another. On the surface of a bowl of water, the water molecules are attracted by the water molecules below and around them more than by the air molecules above. This causes water to form a surface like a membrane. When you float the matchsticks and paper boats in the bowl, they are held in place by the surface tension of the water, which exerts a force in all directions. The addition of the dish soap breaks the surface tension, reducing the pulling force of the water molecules on that side of the matchstick. The attraction from the water molecules on the other side, which are still strongly attracted to each other, pulls the matchstick away from the dish soap and sends it zooming across the water's surface.

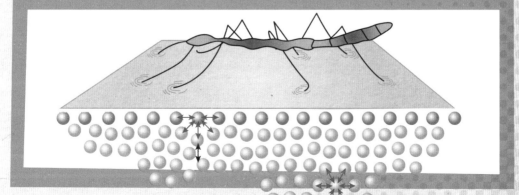

27

GRAVITY-DEFYING WATER BUCKET

Swing a bucket of water overhead—and stay dry!

YOU WILL NEED:
• Plastic bucket
• Water

!

Until you've mastered this trick you should wear a bathing suit or clothes that you don't mind getting soaked—and put that smartphone somewhere safe!

SETUP

This is another experiment that's best done on a hot spring or summer's day, as you may get wet! Fill the bucket around three-quarters full of water, or slightly less if your bucket is big—you'll be swinging it around with one hand, so you don't want it to be too heavy. Stand on the lawn or somewhere in the yard where a big splash is OK.

TESTING

Take hold of the bucket in one hand and swing it swiftly in an arc over your head. It's very important that you swing the bucket quickly. What happens? Now do it more slowly, and a little more slowly again. Keep going until you get a good soaking! If you're in an area where you won't cause damage, try letting go of the bucket at the top of the swing. What happens then?

IN CONCLUSION

If the bucket's moving fast enough, you stay dry: inertia and centripetal force combine to keep the water in the swinging bucket. Sir Isaac Newton's first law of motion (first published in 1686)—sometimes called the law of inertia—states that a still object will stay still and a moving object will carry on moving in the same direction and at the same speed unless an external force acts on them. You swing the bucket up in a circle over your head. The water and bucket, in line with Newton's first law, are set to carry on moving in the direction you've started them traveling. But your arm is exerting a centripetal force, pulling both bucket and water back toward the center. At the same time, gravity is forcing the water down toward your head. While the water is falling, the bucket on the end of your arm is falling, too, so the bucket catches the water. This works so long as you swing the bucket fast enough. Swing too slowly and the water leaves the bucket—and you get drenched.

28

WATERPROOF HANKY

Can a handkerchief really hold back water?

YOU WILL NEED:
- Drinking glass
- Water • Cotton handkerchief

SETUP

Fill the glass right to the brim with water and place the handkerchief over the top. Use your hand to hold it very tightly in place.

TESTING

Making sure you hold the handkerchief tightly all the way round the glass, quickly tip the glass upside down. Hold it up in front of you—or over your friend's head!

Now see what happens if you poke a finger up into the handkerchief across the top of the glass. What if you don't hold the handkerchief so tightly in place? And what happens if you turn the glass onto its side?

You could try mixing detergent or shampoo into the water, experimenting with a few different types. And you might want to see what happens if you use a handkerchief or piece of cloth with a looser weave.

IN CONCLUSION

If you invert an ordinary glass of water, the water falls out as large bubbles of air rise up, replacing the liquid. Here, the cotton handkerchief becomes wet and this prevents air from entering. For air to get into the glass, very small bubbles would have to push up through the mesh of the handkerchief. The tiny bubbles do not have sufficient energy to push the water back, which is held in place by surface tension—the cohesive force between the water molecules attracts them to one another and prevents the surface breaking.

This is how "breathable" waterproof fabrics in hiking jackets work. In between a waterproof outer layer and an insulating inner layer is a thin membrane containing tiny pores. These pores are just large enough to allow water molecules from your sweat to pass out through them, but surface tension prevents raindrops from breaking up and becoming small enough to travel in through them. So you stay dry but your body can "breathe," as water from your sweat can escape.

29

SQUARE BUBBLE

See soap get bent out of shape

YOU WILL NEED:
• Pipe cleaners • Dish soap
• Water
OPTIONAL:
• Bubble wand

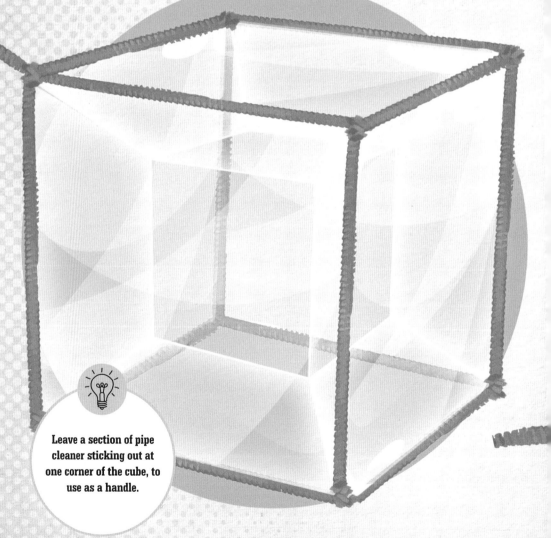

Leave a section of pipe cleaner sticking out at one corner of the cube, to use as a handle.

SETUP

Twist the pipe cleaners together to form a cube. Do this by bending them at right angles and twisting sections around one another. Next, mix up a solution of five parts water to one part dish soap. Mix it together thoroughly but gently, so as not to create too many bubbles.

TESTING

Dip the pipe cleaner cube into the solution and make sure it's well immersed. What happens when you pull it out? See what happens if you gently shake the cube from side to side, or if you dip the cube in and out of the soap mixture several times in succession. What happens if you blow through the bubble mixture in the cube structure? You could also try dipping the cube once and setting it on your patio table, then dipping a wand from a pack of bubbles and using it to blow a bubble downward from just above the cube.

IN CONCLUSION

Water molecules are cohesive—they tend to hold together—and the cohesive force results in surface tension. Bubbles are just air with a thin skin of water on the outside. Water does form bubbles on its own, as you see when you run a faucet, but the water molecules evaporate too quickly for the bubbles to hold together for long.

Adding liquid soap slows down the water's evaporation and reduces its surface tension, making the bubbles' surface more elastic. When you blow air into a water and soap mixture, the air stretches the liquid surface, while cohesion and surface tension work against this by pulling the molecules together. These opposing forces cause the molecules to make a sphere—the shape with the smallest ratio of surface area to volume. The smallest surface area allows the molecules to be as close together as possible. In this demonstration water molecules adhere to the pipe cleaner frame while also sticking together (due to cohesion), and the shape of the frame causes the mixture to adopt a square form.

PART 4

TRICKS OF LIGHT AND WEIGHT

CONTENTS

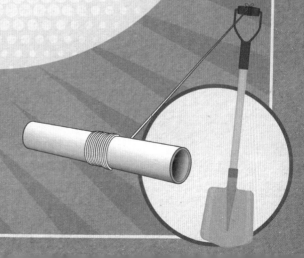

WORLD'S CHEAPEST CAMERA

Explore the physics of pinhole photography

YOU WILL NEED:
- Cylindrical chip can
- Measuring tape • Utility knife • Thumbtack • Tinfoil
- Wax paper • Sticky tape

OPTIONAL:
- Black paper

Mark a point 2in (5cm) up from the metal bottom of the can and then draw a line around the can at that height. Cut neatly around the line so you end up with two cylindrical sections. Use the thumbtack to make a hole in the center of the metal bottom of the can, keeping it as small and neat as possible. Take the lid off the chip can and place it on top of the wax paper, then draw around it and cut out a circle slightly larger than the lid. Tape this in place over the top of the shorter section of the chip can and put the longer piece on top of that. Hold the two parts of the can together and tape them so the whole can is back in its original shape. To keep light out of your camera, wrap tinfoil all the way around the can twice and tape it securely in place. Your camera is ready for use.

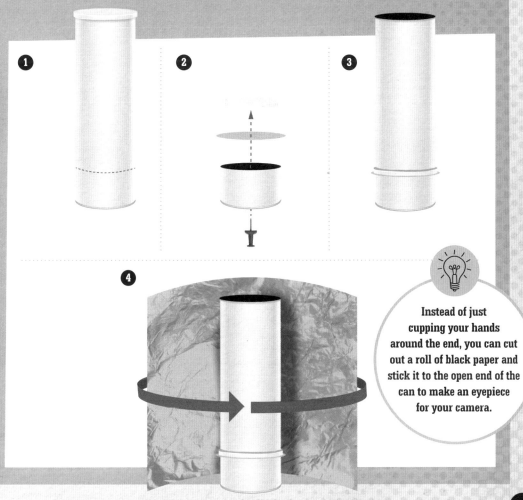

Instead of just cupping your hands around the end, you can cut out a roll of black paper and stick it to the open end of the can to make an eyepiece for your camera.

WORLD'S CHEAPEST CAMERA

TESTING

Hold the open end of the tube to your eye and point the other end in the direction of whatever you want to look at. Cup your hands around the end of the tube and your eye for the best results.

You could ask a friend or family member to wave at you as you look at them through the camera. If they're athletic, you could get them to do a handstand. What do you notice? How clear is the image? What is unusual about it? Move your camera closer to and farther away from your subject. Does the image get sharper and fuzzier?

Try varying the size of the pinhole to see what difference it makes. Or try taking your camera out into the backyard on different days, to see if it works better when the sun is shining or on a dull day.

THE CAMERA OBSCURA

The pinhole camera is itself based on the camera obscura, which has been used by artists since the 16th century. The process by which the light passes through the pinhole and casts an image is therefore known as the camera obscura effect. A camera obscura was simply a darkened room. Light passing through an aperture in the wall cast an entirely lifelike—but upside-down—image on the rear wall. Artists used the camera obscura to learn how to draw and paint using perspective.

Never, under any circumstances, look directly at the sun through your camera!

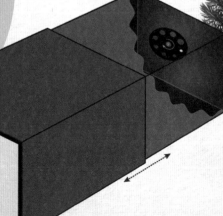

IN CONCLUSION

The image you see on the wax paper-covered "screen" will be upside down. As you move nearer to or farther away from the object you're looking at, you should see the image go in and out of focus. If you experimented with making the pinhole larger, you likely found that the smaller hole created a sharper but dimmer image; a larger hole will let in more light but the image will be increasingly blurred.

Light bounces off the objects we're looking at all the time. Let's say you're looking at a friend standing in the backyard wearing a bright red shirt and bright yellow pants. Many rays of light reflected off the different parts of your friend—his shirt and pants, and, of course, his skin and hair—pass through the pinhole, hit the screen behind as points of light, and together these form an image. Because the rays travel in a straight line as they pass through the small hole, the reflected light from your friend's head will hit the lower part of your camera screen, while the rays from his feet hit the upper part of the screen: so he will look like he's standing upside down. What's more, light from his right hand hits the left-hand part of the screen and light from his left hand hits the screen's right-hand side: he's reversed as well as inverted. When you make the hole in your chip can bigger, more rays can pass through and the points of light overlap on the screen; more light makes the image brighter but the overlapping of the points mean that it becomes blurred.

Our camera does not take pictures, but it is inspired by actual pinhole cameras that can be used to take detailed and beautiful photographs. These pinhole cameras can be as simple as a lightproof box with a pinhole in one side and photographic paper or a piece of film positioned opposite. On the outside of the box, a taped flap of cardboard can be moved to cover or uncover the pinhole, acting as a "shutter" to start and end the exposure of the film or photographic paper. You can get very clear and colorful images from a pinhole camera in this way, so long as the exposure is long—pinhole images often take 20 minutes or so to produce.

PUZZLER!?!

What does the word "camera" mean in the phrase camera obscura?

FIBER-OPTIC SPLASH

Understand the bright science behind hi-tech cables

YOU WILL NEED:
• Empty 68fl oz (2l) plastic bottle • Screwdriver or drill • Water • Flashlight

SETUP

You'll want to do this in a corner of the yard where you don't mind making a splash. Make a small hole in one side of the bottle, about 1in (2.5cm) from the bottom. Put your finger over this hole while you fill the bottle with water. Keep your finger over the hole as you carefully move the bottle and place it on a table or chair in your yard.

If you have a laser pointer, try using this in place of the flashlight.

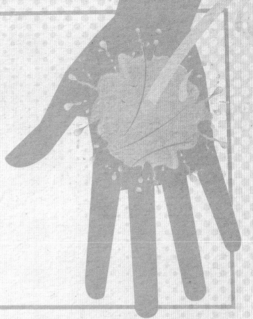

TESTING

When you are ready to release the water, remove your finger from the hole and hold your hand beneath the bottle in the stream of water. Now shine the flashlight so the light passes directly through the hole from which the water is pouring. (You can ask a helper to do this if it's easier.) What happens to the light? Look at where the flashlight is and where the end of the water stream is. Can you explain what's happening?

IN CONCLUSION

The light will follow the curve of the water and make a bright circle on your hand. In fact, the light is traveling in straight lines, but is constantly reflected within the stream of water, due to the phenomenon of total internal reflection. To see this principle in action on a large scale, open your eyes just under the surface of the water in a swimming pool. You'll find that you don't see the sky and people outside; instead, the water surface reflects everything underneath the water. This happens when the angle between the surface and the light direction is shallow, and it's the same thing that's happening in this experiment. The inner surfaces of the curved stream of water act like a mirror, reflecting the light along the inner part of the stream until it hits your hand. Even though the stream of water bends, the light follows it.

Hi-tech fiber-optic cables use a similar method to transmit information, with pulses of light reflected along an inner section of very pure, high-quality glass. At one end of the cable, a computer converts electrical data into light pulses that are sent down the cable by a laser or LED (light-emitting diode). At the other end, a receiving detector converts the light pulses back to electrical data for the computer. You can send more information far more quickly down a fiber-optic cable than through a conventional wire—that's why fiber-optic broadband is so fast.

#32

FROZEN BUBBLES

A cold-weather wonder—crystallized magic

YOU WILL NEED:
- Water • Dish soap
- Corn syrup • Sugar
- Bowl • Plastic straw

OPTIONAL:
- Pipe cleaner
- Small tray

To do this experiment outside, wait for a day that's colder than 10°F (−12°C). A bright day with winter sunshine will give you the best chance of seeing the effects the light creates when it hits the bubbles. If you live somewhere warm, read the additional setup section on page 107 to find out how to make frozen bubbles indoors.

SETUP

We've had several experiments for a hot summer's day or night, but here's one for a frosty morning or early evening in the middle of winter. The day is at its coldest at these times, so your bubbles are more likely to freeze. You also want to avoid breezes, so do this on a still day or somewhere sheltered. Wrap up warm and be prepared to capture the beautiful bubbles on a camera or smartphone.

You need to start preparing this experiment indoors. Gently mix around $^4/_5$ cup (189ml) of water, 2¼ tablespoons of syrup, and 2¼ tablespoons of dish soap in the bowl, then add around 2 tablespoons of the sugar and gently stir the ingredients together. Take your time and don't whisk too vigorously, or you'll whip it up into a mess of bubbles. Once the ingredients are combined, put the mixture in the freezer for around half an hour. A colder mixture will help your bubbles freeze more effectively when you get outside. When you take the mixture out of the freezer, give it a quick stir, then head outside into the cold with a straw.

TESTING

Find a rough surface to blow the bubbles against— perhaps a fence or a shed. If there's snow or ice on the ground or a tabletop, that's ideal. Put the bowl down somewhere flat and then dip the straw into the mixture and blow the bubbles against the wall or rough surface. Be patient—many of the bubbles will burst before they settle. When they do settle, look closely. How are they different from normal bubbles? Why do you think they look like this? How long do the bubbles last? And what happens if you touch one?

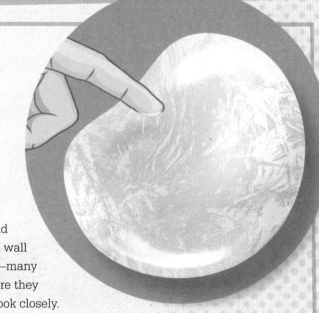

FROZEN BUBBLES

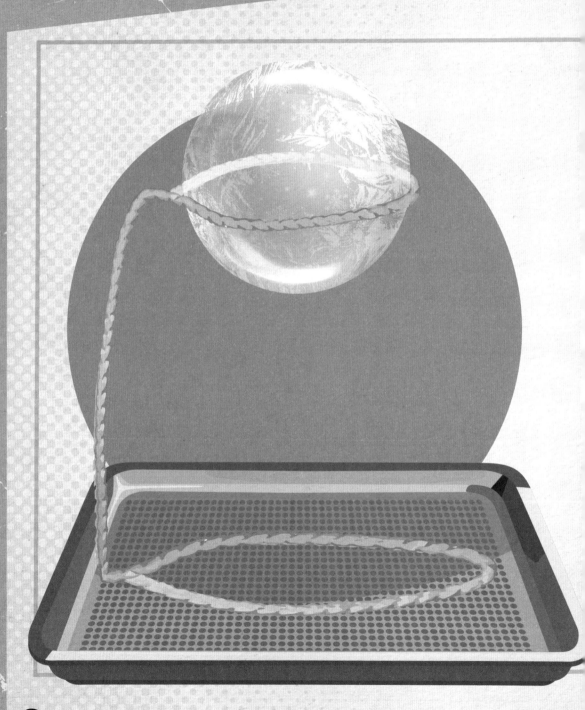

ADDITIONAL SETUP

If you don't live in the right part of the world for very cold weather, or you can't wait for a cold winter's day to try it out, you can do a version of this experiment using your freezer.

For this, take a long pipe cleaner and bend it to make a small hoop at one end and a large hoop at the other. Then fashion this into a little stand, with the large hoop at the bottom and the small hoop above. Place the stand on a small tray. Make up the bubble mixture as in the instructions on page 105, then use a straw to gently blow a bubble onto the smaller hoop of your stand. Very carefully, place the tray in the freezer and leave it for 90 seconds. Open the freezer, pick the little stand up, and gently bring it out. Look closely at the effect on the bubble. How long does the bubble last when you take it out? You can also repeat the experiment and try popping a frozen bubble.

IN CONCLUSION

A soap bubble consists of a layer of water molecules caught between two thin layers of soap molecules. If it's cold enough outside when you blow your bubbles, the layer of water molecules will freeze. If you pay close attention, you can see the ice crystals forming in the layer of water; they seem to skip across the bubble surface. It's a thing of rare beauty— but frail. Cracks form along with the crystals and this gives air molecules trapped inside the bubble a means of escape, so that the pressure within falls suddenly and the bubble collapses. The corn syrup and sugar in the mixture should have the effect of making the bubbles last longer, and they also form crystal patterns while the bubbles are freezing.

When you pop the bubble gently with your finger or the end of the straw, you might see it seem to crumple and deflate rather than pop as a bubble would on a summer's day. Alternatively, if you pop it more forcefully, you'll probably see the solid sections blow apart.

33

MAKE A SUNDIAL

A shadow clock without the tick-tock

SETUP

Start first thing on a sunny day. Hammer the nail into the center of the wooden board so that the nail sticks out vertically. It's important that the board doesn't move, so secure it in place with a couple of weights or stones.

IN CONCLUSION

The sun appears to move westward across the sky as Earth turns eastward on its polar axis. The Earth rotates on its axis once every 24 hours. On the sundial we track the hour-by-hour, minute-by-minute movement of a shadow cast by the sun. The shadow of the nail points westward as the sun rises in the east; through the morning, it shortens and comes to point north; then after noon it lengthens and points eastward.

The use of the sundial to tell time goes back 3,500–4,000 years to the ancient Babylonians and Egyptians. While ancient people thought the Earth was stationary and that the sun really did move across the sky each day, we know that the Earth rotates around the sun and spins on its axis as it does so, and this is what makes the sun appear to move.

TESTING

When it's the top of the hour (for example, 8 a.m. or 9 a.m.) pencil in a mark on the board indicating where the shadow of the nail falls. Repeat this every 30 and 60 minutes throughout the day. Next to each mark, note the time that it corresponds to. At the end of the day, use the ruler to draw lines connecting the marks to the center of the board. You now have a sundial.

Depending on where you live, you may switch to or from daylight saving time during the year and the sundial will need to be adjusted, by changing the time that corresponds with each mark on the dial. For example, the mark that matches 9 a.m. at one time of year may correspond to 8 a.m. at another. Your sundial is calibrated for your specific longitude and latitude. If you try to use it elsewhere, say, in a different state, you'll have to adapt it.

Anything you can set up to cast a shadow will work for this experiment. You could erect a bamboo stick in your lawn and mark out the shadow positions on the ground around it with pebbles.

34

SWEET, SWEET LIGHT

A strange glow from sugar

YOU WILL NEED:
- Sugar cubes
- Pair of pliers

The darker it is, the more chance you have of seeing the results.

SETUP

This experiment is best carried out on a dark night when there isn't much moonlight. Choose the darkest spot in your backyard—away from any streetlights or other light sources. Before it's fully dark, lay out the sugar cubes and pliers on the table in your yard. Return when it's dark and give your eyes a chance to become accustomed to the lack of light.

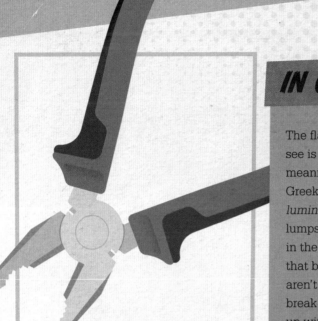

IN CONCLUSION

The flashing of luminous blue you see is called triboluminescence—meaning "rubbing light," from the Greek *tribein*, to rub, and Latin *lumin*, light. As you crush the sugar lumps with your pliers, the crystals in the lump fracture. Scientists think that because these sugar crystals aren't quite symmetrical, when you break them in half, one half ends up with a slightly positive charge, the other slightly negative. The difference in the charge of the two halves causes sparks to jump from one half to the other. The sparking excites air molecules, and when the air particles return to their usual state, they release energy, which we see in the form of a blue glow.

Triboluminescence is not well understood, but it can be thought of as lightning on a small scale. Lightning is formed when a stream of electrons pass through the air, which excites the air molecules. When the molecules return to their usual state, we see the energy emitted in the form of light.

TESTING

Pick up a sugar cube in one hand and take the pliers in the other. Placing the cube between the pincer heads of the pliers, squeeze as hard as you can. Keep your eyes peeled. What do you see? What color is produced? Repeat the experiment with a few more sugar cubes to see if the result is always the same.

If you can't find any pliers, you can achieve the same effect by crushing the sugar with the flat bottom of a tumbler.

SELF-SUPPORTING BRIDGE

Designed by the great Leonardo da Vinci

YOU WILL NEED:

FOR SIDE PIECES:
- 10 pieces of wood about 2 × 4in (5 × 10cm) and 4ft (1.2m) long

FOR CROSSPIECES:
- Five rounded pieces of wood about 1in (2cm) in diameter and 2ft 6in (76cm) long

OPTIONAL:
- Big bag of jumbo craft sticks

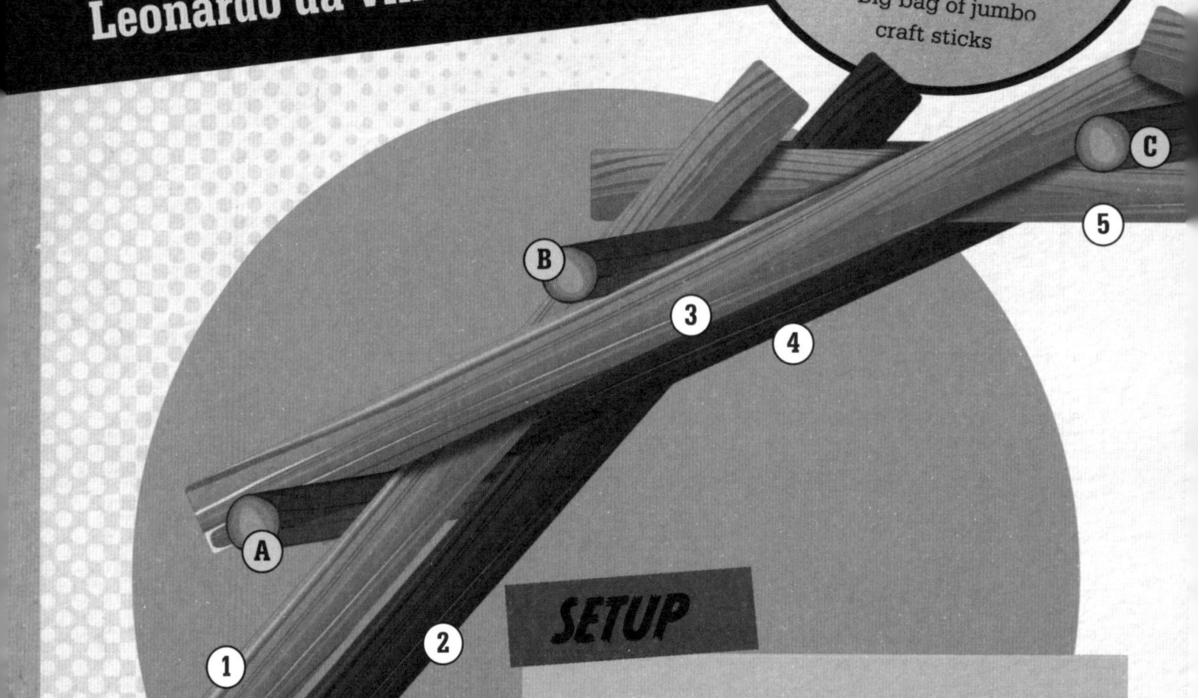

C

5

B

3

4

A

1

2

SETUP

You can find videos showing how to build a self-supporting bridge online. Check out the "Further reading" section at the back of this book for a suggested video.

For the main setup all you need is your lengths of wood, patience, and a little scientific brilliance—borrowed from Renaissance polymath Leonardo da Vinci. Gather together the 10 side pieces and five crosspieces on the lawn or a large, open, paved area of the backyard. You'll need a lot of room for this demonstration. The pieces of wood are given letters (crosspieces: A–E) and numbers (side pieces: 1–10) in the description to make it easier to understand how to put this structure together. You may find it helpful to pencil numbers on your pieces of wood before you start building.

TESTING

Lay two side pieces (1 and 2) so that they're parallel. Put one crosspiece (A) horizontally across both, about halfway down. Lay two more side pieces (3 and 4) with their left-hand ends on top of crosspiece A. Lift the right ends of 1 and 2 and place another crosspiece (B) underneath 1 and 2 but on top of 3 and 4. Lay two more side pieces (5 and 6) within 3 and 4, with their left ends on top of crosspiece B. Now lift the right ends of 3 and 4 and lay another crosspiece (C) underneath 3 and 4 and on top of 5 and 6. Lay two more side pieces (7 and 8), with their left ends resting on crosspiece C. Lift the right ends of pieces 5 and 6 and put another crosspiece (D) underneath the right-hand ends of 5 and 6 and on top of pieces 7 and 8. Place the last two side pieces (9 and 10) parallel to 7 and 8, but this time outside. Lift the right-hand ends of 7 and 8 and place the final crosspiece (E) underneath 7 and 8 and on top of 9 and 10.

Once your bridge is built, you should be able to walk across it. Try going across slowly on your hands and knees first to check that it's stable.

SELF-SUPPORTING BRIDGE

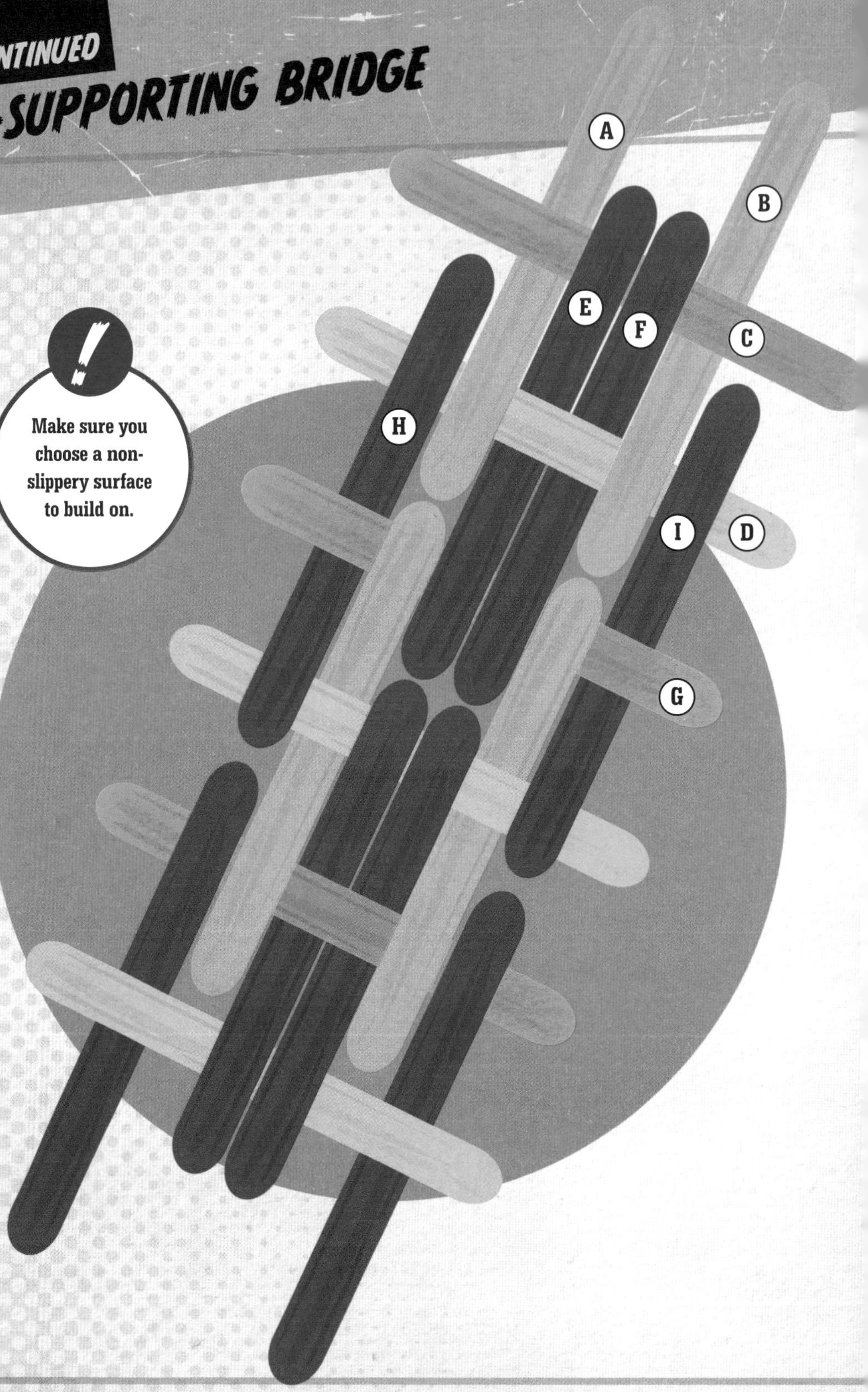

(A)

(B)

(E) (F)

(C)

(H)

(I) (D)

(G)

! Make sure you choose a non-slippery surface to build on.

If you haven't got the wood or the space to build a large version of the bridge, you can make a mini version on a table or small paved area using craft sticks. It's best to use jumbo craft sticks for this (you can find these online or in art and craft supply stores), but you can also use the narrower sticks you find in popsicles. As with the main experiment, you may find it useful to label the sticks you're going to start building with (A–I).

Take two sticks (A and B) and lay them parallel to each other. Place a third stick (C) beneath A and B at one end and a fourth (D) across them, roughly halfway down. Feed two more sticks (E and F) underneath (C), so that they sit on top of D. Slide G beneath the end of E and F. Feed two more sticks (H and I), so that they sit on top of D and under G. You'll find the bridge raises itself naturally up off the table. Extend the bridge by adding more vertical sticks and feeding in more horizontal sticks. Once you have built the bridge, test its strength by pressing down with your fingers on the middle of the span. Look to make sure the pieces are fitting together well and none are misaligned.

IN CONCLUSION

Gravity and friction hold this self-supporting bridge together—it's a masterpiece of applied physics. Gravity pulls the pieces of wood downward against one another and friction stops them from slipping. In fact, the more weight that is added to the bridge, the more the wood pieces are pushed together and the stronger the bridge becomes. The bridge can bear weight from above, but it will collapse easily if you push or pull it from the side.

Renaissance man Leonardo da Vinci—the artist behind the iconic paintings *The Last Supper* and the *Mona Lisa*, but arguably just as gifted as a scientist—designed the self-supporting bridge while working for the celebrated Borgia family in the late 1400s. He planned for it to be made with logs and called it the "bridge of safety." His version used notches in the logs for the crosspieces to fit into, but the design works using only friction. We don't know for sure if it was ever used, but it seems highly likely that mobile late-15th-century armies would have taken advantage of a design that made it possible to build a secure, weight-bearing bridge over a river using only a few logs.

36

JAR RACE

Rolling is different from falling

YOU WILL NEED:
• Jar of jelly • Two empty jars of the same shape and size • Long table • Long pole (e.g. broom handle) or piece of string • One or two books • Cushions

SETUP

Use one or two books to prop up one end of the table so that it slopes down from one end to the other. Your table should be about 2 yards (1.8m) long and drop around 2in (2.5cm) from one end to the other. Put cushions on the ground at the lower end. Fill one of your jars with water so you have one jar full of jelly, one jar full of water, and one empty jar, and make sure the lids are screwed onto all the jars.

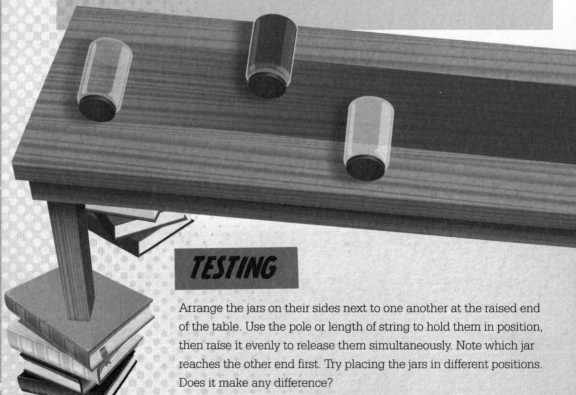

TESTING

Arrange the jars on their sides next to one another at the raised end of the table. Use the pole or length of string to hold them in position, then raise it evenly to release them simultaneously. Note which jar reaches the other end first. Try placing the jars in different positions. Does it make any difference?

IN CONCLUSION

You might expect the jars to reach the end together—after all, if you drop a large pebble and a lighter stone from a height they hit the ground at the same time. But rolling's different to falling. The jars roll at varying speeds: the water-filled jar is the fastest, the jelly-filled jar is second, and the empty jar is slowest. This is partly due to differences in how mass is distributed in the different jars. An object with more mass around the outside (the empty jar) accelerates more slowly than one with more mass toward the center (the jelly jar). In the empty jar, more of the overall mass of the object has to be accelerated into a rolling motion than the jar filled with the jelly, so it travels more slowly.

The water in the rolling water-filled jar essentially stays still, with the glass rotating around it, as if all the mass was at the center of the turning jar. Less of the overall mass has to be accelerated into the roll, in comparison to the jelly. So, the water-filled jar rolls fastest.

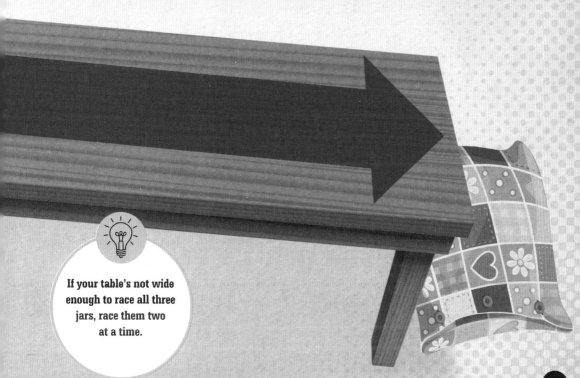

If your table's not wide enough to race all three jars, race them two at a time.

37

TUBE FLIP

The science that makes a baseball curve in flight

YOU WILL NEED:
• Spade • Lightweight PVC tube • Elastic around 3 yards (2.7m) long

SETUP

Dig your spade into the lawn or a patch of earth in an open spot in your yard where you won't hit anything breakable. Tie one end of the elastic to the spade handle and, pulling the elastic taut, roll the remaining elastic around and around the center of your PVC tube, with the elastic joining the tube from underneath rather than around the top. Leave about 1 yard (0.9m) of elastic between the tube and the spade.

TESTING

Holding the tube with the elastic wrapped around it, stand a yard behind the spade. Make sure the elastic linking the spade handle to your roll is taut and hold the elastic in position on the tube with your finger. Make sure nothing is in the line of fire, then let go. What happens? Try winding the elastic more or less tightly. You can also experiment using tubes of varying lengths and made of different materials. Do these variations affect how far the tube flies?

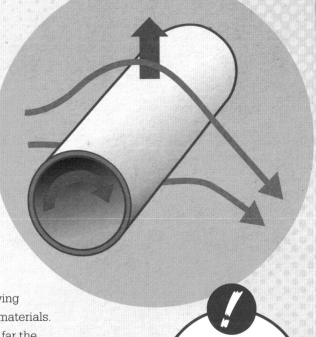

Make sure there's lots of open space and nobody is standing in front of the spade, as your tube will go flying forward.

IN CONCLUSION

As the elastic runs out and the tube is released, the tube should flip upward as it flies. This is the result of the Magnus effect, discovered by the German scientist Heinrich Gustav Magnus in around 1850. Air adheres to the spinning tube and, because of the way the tube is spinning, it adheres more to the tube's top (which is spinning in the direction of the airflow) than to its bottom (which is spinning against the direction of airflow). This combination means the air is pushed downward by the tube and, because for each reaction there is an equal and opposite reaction (as we know from Newton's third law of motion), the tube is pushed upward. This is the science behind the spin that a tennis player or baseball pitcher puts on a ball to make it swerve at the last minute.

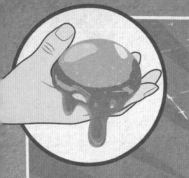

PART 5

FUTURE SHOCK
AND
SIMPLY WEIRD

CONTENTS

EGG IN A BOTTLE

An eggstraordinary squeeze!

To help the egg slip inside, you could rub a little cooking oil around the inside of the bottle neck.

SETUP

This is a great trick to amuse friends. Tell them it's a classic science demo that's at least 100 years old. Hard-boil an egg, then leave it to cool in a bowl of cold water. Once it's cool, crack the shell and peel it off. Find a glass bottle with a neck slightly narrower than the egg. If you have a traditional milk bottle that will be perfect. Fold a strip of paper so it will fit through the bottle neck and get some matches or a lighter ready.

TESTING

Set the egg in the bottle neck, to demonstrate that it won't fit through. Now remove the egg, light the strip of paper, and drop the burning paper into the bottle. Pop the egg back on top of the bottle neck and watch closely. Why is the egg moving? What happens once the flame has gone out?

IN CONCLUSION

The difference in air pressure between the outside and inside of the bottle pushes the egg through the narrow neck and into the bottle. At the beginning of the demonstration the air pressure outside and inside the bottle is the same. The burning strip of paper you drop into the bottle heats the air inside, causing it to expand. This expanding air increases the pressure in the bottle, so now the air pressure within the bottle is greater than outside and some air escapes. Did you see the egg wobble after you first set it on top? That was because some of the heated air pushed it out of the way as it left the bottle. After the flame goes out, the air in the bottle cools and contracts. Now the pressure outside is greater than inside. This makes the air outside push to get into the bottle and, as it does so, it forces the egg through the bottle neck. Although the egg is hard-boiled, it is still soft and so it can squeeze through the opening. What would happen if you did not remove the shell?

HOVERDISK

Make your own hovercraft using a CD and a balloon

YOU WILL NEED:
• Disk, e.g. CD or DVD • Pop-up sports cap from a drinks bottle
• Adhesive putty • Balloon
OPTIONAL:
• Balloons of different sizes
• Glue or sticky tape
• Small objects to balance on the disk

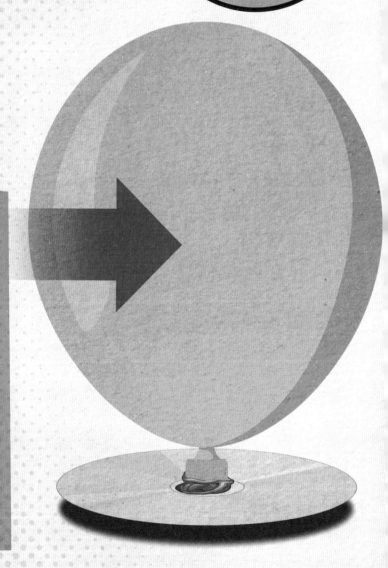

SETUP

Roll some adhesive putty into a short sausage that's long enough to make a circle around the bottle top. Lift the pop-top of the bottle top as if you were going to have a drink from it, and use the putty to stick it over the hole in the center of the disk. Set it down on the backyard table. Inflate the balloon and twist the end to stop the air escaping.

TESTING

Untwist the balloon and stretch it over the bottle top, then let go. As the air from the balloon lifts the disk, give the contraption a gentle push to make it travel across the tabletop. How far can you make it slide? (If you find that the adhesive putty isn't strong enough to hold the cap to the disk, you could try using glue or electrical tape to stick them together.)

What happens if you use a larger balloon? Can you balance small objects on the disk to make them hover?

PUZZLER!?!

True or false: The idea of hovering vehicles dates back to the 18th century.

IN CONCLUSION

The hoverdisk demonstrates how an air cushion substantially reduces friction when a vehicle (here, the disk) moves across a surface. The air released as the balloon deflates passes through the bottle top and the central hole of the CD, pushes down on the table below and lifts the disk up a little way. This enables the disk to move across the tabletop without touching it. When you push the disk lightly it is able to travel with reduced friction for a short distance.

Full-size vehicles use this reduced-resistance movement on an air cushion over both water and land. English engineer Sir Christopher Cockerell developed the first commercially viable hovercraft in the late 1950s, and for many years, from the mid-1960s to the year 2000, hovercrafts carried British vacationers—and their cars and caravans—across the English Channel to France. There have also been hovertrains (one still carries passengers in an Austrian ski resort called Serfaus), hoverbarges for moving loads over mixed water and marshland, and even hover-vacuum cleaners, which have no wheels and move on a cushion of air.

EXTRACT DNA

Isolate fruit DNA with this simple process

YOU WILL NEED:
• Soft pear or other fruit (see tip box on page 128) • Isopropyl alcohol • Water • Dish soap • Salt • Bowl • Knife • Spoon • Pestle • Two glass jars • Tweezers • Sieve • Coffee filter paper (or paper towel) • Small dish or plate

OPTIONAL:
• Pineapple juice

You can usually pick up isopropyl alcohol at a drugstore.

Do you have a pear or apple tree in your backyard? If so, perfect! If not, you could use strawberries from your greenhouse or an onion from your vegetable patch. If you don't have any fruit or vegetables growing in your backyard, then shop–bought varieties will work just as well.

First, pop your bottle of isopropyl alcohol in the freezer. Then lay out all your equipment on the backyard table. Mix 6 tablespoons of water, 2 tablespoons of dish soap, and ¼ teaspoon of salt in a small jar, stirring them together gently so you don't create bubbles. We're going to call this the "extracting solution." Next, take a nice ripe pear and peel and slice it. (If you're using other fruit or vegetables, prepare these in the same way.) Finally, line a fine sieve with wet coffee filter paper. (You can use wetted kitchen paper if you don't have coffee filter paper.)

TESTING

Chop the slice of pear into tiny pieces and put it into the bowl, then mash it up well using a spoon or pestle. Add the pear mush to the extracting solution and mix them together—but be careful not to make bubbles as you stir. Pour the fruit and extracting solution through the paper-lined sieve and into the other jar; this will get rid of all the remaining solid bits of pear. Fetch your isopropyl alcohol from the freezer and very carefully pour the ice-cold alcohol into the filtrate you collected, tilting the jar as you do so, so that the two don't mix. You need to finish with roughly the same amount of alcohol and fruit mixture.

What do you see? There should be a whitish substance visible where the alcohol and the fruit mixture meet. If you can see this pale substance, take your tweezers and carefully try to tease it up and out of the liquid. You can then put it on a dish so that you can examine it more closely.

EXTRACT DNA

IN CONCLUSION

The whitish fibers you pull out with the tweezers are strands of pear DNA. Deoxyribonucleic acid (DNA) is in every plant and animal cell and determines the organism's genetic traits. Each cell has an identical copy of the organism's DNA: the genome. Normally, the DNA is contained within the nuclei of cells. The extracting mixture is designed to "liberate" the DNA from the nuclei—the dish soap breaks down the cell membranes and the salt unravels the protein chains that bind the nucleic acids, thereby releasing the DNA.

When you add the alcohol to the fruit and extracting fluid mixture, the DNA becomes visible. The reason you can't see the DNA until you add the alcohol is that DNA dissolves in water but is not soluble in alcohol. So when you add the alcohol the DNA precipitates out of the solution, becoming visible and tangible—you can even pick it up with tweezers.

There's an extra step you can add to remove proteins that remain bound to the DNA. Before adding the alcohol, add one part pineapple juice for every five parts of the fruit and extracting fluid mixture and leave it for five minutes. The pineapple juice removes extra proteins, so adding it will give you a purer solution, and you'll be able to see the DNA more clearly.

This is a backyard version of the biotechnology often used in DNA extraction kits in science laboratories. Like our demonstration, these kits often use detergent to open plant and animal cells and alcohol to precipitate DNA out of solution so it can be studied.

You could also try this using other fruit or vegetables, such as:
• Banana • Apple
• Strawberry • Kiwi
• Onion • Spinach
• Peas

PUZZLER!?!

True or false: If you unraveled the DNA in your body it would reach farther than the sun?

GENOME IN THE STRUCTURE OF DNA

The genome (gene + chromosomes) is the aggregate of all the hereditary information of the organism.

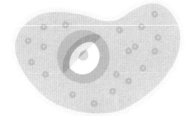

The nucleus of the human cell contains 23 pairs of chromosomes.

Each of the pairs of chromosomes contains a separate linear double-stranded DNA molecule.

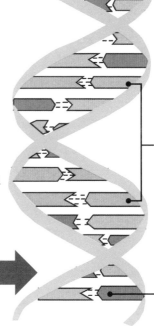

The size of the gene in the chromosome is about 50,000 pairs of nucleotides.

A pair of nucelotides.

Size of DNA:
- In the largest chromosome: 250 million pairs of nucleotides
- In the smallest: 47 million pairs of nucleotides

ELECTRIFIED SLIME

Slime sits up and pays attention

YOU WILL NEED:
- Cornstarch • Vegetable oil
- Cup • Balloon • Tablespoon

OPTIONAL:
- Wool item, e.g. sweater

SETUP

Although this is not a full-on messy experiment, you might end up dropping some of the mixture on the ground, so mix it up in a part of the backyard where you don't mind making a bit of a mess. Add around three tablespoons of cornstarch to the cup and mix it with enough vegetable oil to make a thick liquid with the consistency of double cream. Inflate the balloon and tie a knot in the end.

TESTING

Take the balloon and rub one side of it against your hair or a woolen item, such as a sweater, for 10–20 seconds. Now hold the balloon in one hand and use the other hand to spoon some of the mixture out of the cup. Hold the balloon close to the spoon and allow the thick, creamy paste to drip from the tablespoon back into the cup. Do you notice anything unusual?

Try turning the balloon around and holding the spoon and mixture close to the part of it you did not rub against your hair or the wool sweater. What happens now?

IN CONCLUSION

Did you find that the paste thickened when it dripped close to the balloon—and even moved toward it? This is electrostatics at work. When you rub the balloon on your hair or something woolen electrons (negatively charged particles) move from your hair or the woolen item to the balloon, leaving that part of the balloon negatively charged. In the paste there are many tiny cornstarch particles, each with equal negative and positive charges. When the negatively charged balloon is brought close to the paste, the negative charges in the particles are repelled from the balloon, while the positive charges are pulled toward it. This movement of particles makes the paste thicken near the balloon and move toward it. The oil in the mixture is important because it is an insulator and does not conduct the charge. Without the oil, the charge would pass from particle to particle rather than making the particles move.

The rubber of the balloon is an electrical insulator and resists the movement of electric charge through it, so only the part you rubbed retains the charge and attracts the mixture.

#42
MEGA-FLUBBER

A party-size backyard slime attack

YOU WILL NEED:
• 10 cups (2.4l) white liquid glue • 12½ cups (3l) warm water • Food dye
• 20 tablespoons borax
• Two large containers, e.g. buckets • Spoon
OPTIONAL:
• Glitter

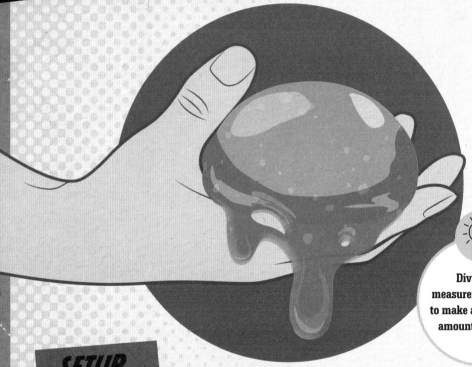

Divide our measurements by 10 to make a one-person amount of flubber

SETUP

This is another experiment that requires old clothes and a corner of the backyard where you don't mind making a mega mess. Measure out 12½ cups (3l) of warm water. You're going to use this to make two separate mixtures. Mix together 10 cups (2.4l) of white glue and 7½ cups (1.8l) of warm water in a bucket or other large container. Make sure they are well combined. In a separate container, mix together 20 tablespoons of borax and 5 cups (1.2l) of warm water. Add a couple of drops of food dye—and a sprinkle of glitter if you want to make a real party-slime.

TESTING

To make your flubber, combine the two mixtures and stir them together well. The resulting substance gets quite thick, so you'll probably want to put the spoon aside and start mixing with your hands. Knead it really well. What does the result look like?

All that's left is to let your party guests loose on the slime—flubber is great fun to play around with. Try putting it in a container, tipping it out, stretching it, or making a handprint in it. Can you make a ball of flubber? Does it bounce?

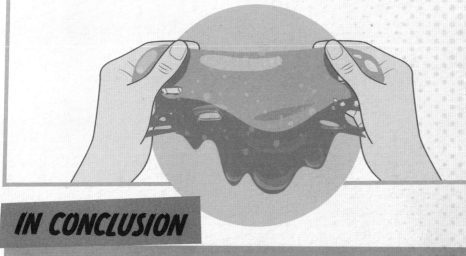

IN CONCLUSION

The chemical reaction between the borax (also known as sodium borate or sodium tetraborate) and the white glue creates the substance we call flubber, which is highly flexible and malleable. The white glue is a polymer, a substance made up of long chains of repeating particles, and the linking together of these polymer chains is the key to flubber. Usually, these chains are unconnected in white glue, so the glue behaves as a liquid. However, when you mix the white glue with the borax, a process called cross-linking happens, in which the borax causes the long chains of particles to link together. When these polymer chains are connected, the substance behaves more like a solid. You can make thicker or thinner flubber by changing the amount of borax mixed into your white glue mixture.

If you're feeling peckish, you can even find recipes for edible flubber online. This is made by heating a can of condensed milk with a tablespoon of cornstarch and adding food dye, before leaving the mixture to cool.

EGG WALK

Try literally walking on eggshells

This experiment is definitely best done outside—things could get messy!

SETUP

Check that none of the eggs are broken or cracked and that they are all aligned the same way—with their more pointy ends facing upward. Lay out the egg cartons in two rows on the ground.

TESTING

Take off your socks and shoes. Ask your helper to partly support your weight as you place one foot on one box of eggs, then the other on the box alongside it. Now your friend can let go. Walk slowly forward, keeping your feet as flat as you can. What happens?

Try turning all the eggs the other way up and walking over them again. Next, test how much weight the eggs can take by piling books on top of them. Experiment with putting a piece of plywood or a tile over the eggs before you add the books. How many books can you add before the eggs sustain some damage?

Try putting the squeeze on an egg: hold it in your palm and close your fingers all around it. Now squeeze! What happens?

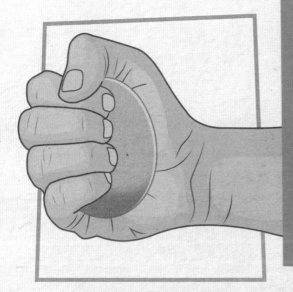

IN CONCLUSION

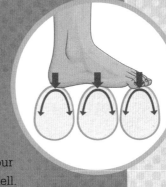

The eggshells are able to withstand your weight as you walk across them because their arched shape distributes the pressure of your feet across the shell. The arch is one of the strongest architectural forms, and the eggshell is strongest at its arched end—as you probably found out, it doesn't matter whether the more pointed ends are all facing up or down. It is important that the surface the eggs presented is as even as possible, so your weight is distributed as widely as possible. This is why they all need to be aligned the same way.

The eggshell is immensely strong so long as pressure is spread over the surface. If you apply pressure at a particular point—for example, tapping the egg against the edge of a bowl—the shell will break easily. An adult hen can sit on an egg without crushing it, but a little chick can break out from inside by tapping with its beak.

#44

HOT ICE SCULPTURES

Instant ice crystals that are hot to the touch

YOU WILL NEED:
- White vinegar • Baking soda • Saucepan • Gas barbecue or camping stove • Spoon • Glass jar • Plastic wrap (if your jar doesn't have a lid) • Plastic tray

OPTIONAL:
- Plastic sheeting • Bowl • Chopstick

SETUP

Put the saucepan on your backyard table and pour in 4 cups (946ml) of vinegar. Add four tablespoons of baking soda a little at a time and carefully mix the ingredients together. Go slow when adding the baking soda to the vinegar—add it too fast and you risk the pan overflowing with foam. Set the solution on your gas barbecue, if you have one, or use a camping stove. Boil the mixture on medium heat until crystals start to form around the edges of the pan—this could take up to an hour. Once you see crystals forming, take the liquid off the heat and pour it into a glass jar. Is the liquid clear? If you see crystals, add a little vinegar until they have dissolved. Now screw the lid on the jar to prevent further evaporation. (You could cover it with plastic wrap if you don't have a lid for your jar.) Place the covered jar in the refrigerator to cool for 45 minutes. Meanwhile, look at the saucepan. You should be able to see crystals left in the bottom and around the edges of the pan—these are crystals of sodium acetate. You may need these later, so don't wash them away just yet.

TESTING

Once your liquid has cooled, carefully retrieve your jar from the refrigerator and bring it outside. Set down a plastic tray and slowly pour some of the cooled solution onto it. What happens? Pour a little more onto the same spot and notice what happens now. Keep pouring onto the same spot and see what crazy shapes you can create. Does it matter how fast you pour? If the solution does not crystallize, try adding a few of the sodium acetate crystals from the saucepan. If ice sculpture "towers" are forming in the dish, touch them to see how they feel. What do you notice?

If you find that the crystallization does not work, you may need to repeat the process. Add a little more vinegar to your mixture, heat it again until a skin forms, cool the mixture again, and then add a sodium acetate crystal or a little baking soda to kick-start the crystallization process when you pour.

You don't have to make the crystal towers in a tray—you could cover your backyard table with some plastic sheeting.

Hot ice is recyclable—you can re-melt the "ice" and repeat the demonstration.

ADDITIONAL SETUP

To experiment further, pour some of the cooled liquid from the refrigerated jar into a bowl and then touch the surface of the liquid with a spoon. What happens? Feel the outside of the bowl. What do you notice? What happens if you touch the surface of the liquid with your finger instead?

You can also try adding a few of the sodium acetate crystals that formed on the sides of the saucepan. Scrape these up with the end of a chopstick and sink the chopstick into the liquid. What happens?

IN CONCLUSION

The baking soda and vinegar reaction creates bubbles of carbon dioxide gas and a solution of sodium acetate and water. When you heat this mixture you boil off most of the water and increase the concentration of sodium acetate in the solution. When we put the solution in the refrigerator, it is chilled below the temperature at which it would normally turn solid: it becomes a supercooled liquid. Then when you touch a crystal to the solution or pour it out, it crystallizes instantly, forming beautiful towers of hot ice. If you pour too fast, you may find that the crystals spread out flat rather than building on top of one another.

You should see crystals begin to form if you touch a spoon or your finger to the surface of the supercooled liquid. This is because touching the liquid produces a nucleation site at which crystallization can begin. The process of crystallization gives off heat—it's an exothermic process—so you will feel the bowl or the "ice" itself to be warm.

You can buy reusable hand warmers that use the heat given off by sodium acetate crystallization to generate warmth. The hand warmers contain metal strips and when these are bent they release molecules that provide nucleation sites. You can heat the hand warmer in a pan of water to "reset" it. This process liquefies the crystals and then you can set off the exothermic reaction all over again.

45

TRAY, TRAY, GONE

See a Styrofoam™ tray disappear before your eyes

YOU WILL NEED:
- Aluminum pie tin or glass dish • Acetone
- Styrofoam™ tray (one takeout food might be served in)

OPTIONAL:
- Alcohol or turpentine

SETUP

This demonstration has to be done in a well-ventilated spot, so the backyard is ideal. Place the pie tin or glass dish on the ground or on a patio table, then carefully pour in enough acetone to cover the bottom. It doesn't need to be deep.

Be careful: acetone is highly flammable.

IN CONCLUSION

Styrofoam™ is a trade name for polystyrene, a polymer consisting of a long chain of molecules, and acetone is a highly effective organic solvent. When the polymer meets the acetone, the polymer begins to break down. However, Styrofoam™ is around 95 percent air (air is injected into the polystyrene when it is manufactured to make it an effective packing and insulating material). The air is released when the acetone breaks down the bonds in the polymer, and the Styrofoam™ loses its structure and seems to disappear. Its remaining molecules become part of the acetone solution.

There are several fun party tricks you can do using this chemical reaction. For example, if you have piles of Styrofoam™ packing "peanuts" at home, one impressive trick is to feed handfuls of these into a small beaker of acetone, then watch them seemingly disappear into nothing, handful after handful. Another—slightly more disturbing—demonstration involves placing a Styrofoam™ head in a dish of acetone then watching it disappear…

TESTING

Place the Styrofoam™ tray in the acetone in the center of the dish and call a few people around to watch what happens. They may not be able to believe their eyes! Does it make any difference if you try different Styrofoam™ objects, such as a cup, for example? How about if you switch the acetone for alcohol or turpentine?

#46

VANISHING TABLECLOTH

Yank a tablecloth away without disturbing anything—voila!

YOU WILL NEED:
- Table • Thin tablecloth without a sewn hem • Place setting (e.g. plates, cutlery, glasses)

OPTIONAL:
- Plastic place setting (e.g. plates, cutlery, glasses)

You may want to practice using a plastic place setting until you get the hang of this trick.

SETUP

Spread the tablecloth out over one end of your table. The cloth needs to be large enough to cover about 2ft (60cm) of table and leave some material hanging over the end. Lay the plates, cutlery, and glasses on the table.

TESTING

Take hold of the overhanging piece of tablecloth, bending down so your hands are below the level of the table. Pull sharply, straight down, parallel with the table legs. What happens? You may need to practice a few times to get the hang of this, but after a few goes you'll be confident enough to make this a party trick, or to get a friend to film you doing it and share it via social media.

If you do master the trick, try varying the table, using one with a different surface, or try different types of tablecloths.

IN CONCLUSION

The law of inertia—described by English physicist Sir Isaac Newton in the first of his three laws of motion—is the key to understanding this trick. According to Newton's explanation, inertia is the tendency of an object to stay where it is so long as no force acts on it to move it, and for a moving object to remain moving at the same speed unless a force acts on it to speed it up, slow it down, or stop it. Here, the force you apply in pulling the tablecloth is not directly applied to the plates, cutlery, and glasses, and is not enough to move them, so they stay where they are.

Don't forget friction, though. When you pull the tablecloth it will generate friction between the table and the cloth and between the cloth and the place setting, and, if friction is significant, this frictional force will be enough to move the place setting. This demonstration therefore works best with a smooth tabletop and a thin tablecloth, to reduce friction.

#47 ⚠️

VORTEX CANNON

Save your breath— blow out candles by hand

YOU WILL NEED:
- Paper cup • Balloon
- Rubber band or sticky tape
- Scissors • Small candles or tea lights • Matches or lighter • Cotton balls

SETUP

Measure the diameter of the opening at the top of the cup and then use scissors to cut a round hole in the base of the cup that is half the size of this opening or smaller. Blow up the balloon and let it deflate, to make it more flexible. Tie the end of the empty balloon and cut the balloon in half horizontally—keep the half with the knot. Line up a few candles or tea lights on the backyard table and light them. Line up a few cotton balls on a different part of the table.

TESTING

Fit the balloon over the open end of the cup, with the knot facing outward. Tape it in place or fix it securely with the rubber band—you want it to be airtight. Turn the cup so the balloon is facing you and point the hole in the bottom of the cup at the candles from around 18in (46cm) away. Pull on the balloon knot and let go. What happens? Try doing the same thing but closer to and farther away from the candles. Over what distance does the vortex flame extinguisher work? Now try firing the device at the row of cotton balls to see what happens.

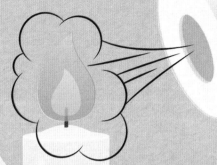

If you can access a smoke machine you can make vortex smoke rings. Just fill the cup with smoke, then fire the cannon.

IN CONCLUSION

Your vortex flame extinguisher should send the cotton balls flying and extinguish the candles from as far as 2–2½ft (61–76cm) away. When you pull and release the balloon knot, you send a jet of air through the hole you cut in the other end of the cup. When this fast-moving air exits the cup, its outer ring of air slows down and circles back in on itself as it encounters the air outside. This forms a donut-shaped vortex spinning around its center. The vortex has an upward air current on one side and a downward current on the other, and these combine to propel the central jet of air further, so you can move the cotton balls or extinguish the candles from surprisingly far away.

You can make an even simpler vortex extinguisher using a plastic bottle (squeeze the sides sharply to blow air out of the opening) or a well-sealed cardboard box with a narrow hole cut in one side (hit the sides and see what happens).

INSTANT ICE

Watch ice crystals form before your eyes

YOU WILL NEED:
- Two 68fl oz (2l) bottles of purified water • Two ice buckets
- Big bag of ice cubes
- Rock salt • Thermometer
- Side dish • Glass jug

OPTIONAL:
- Drinking glass
- Two additional 68fl oz (2l) bottles of purified water

Instead of using ice buckets you can cool the bottles of purified water by putting them directly in the freezer. Set the freezer to around −11°F (−24°C), give it a couple of hours to cool, then put the bottles in there for just under 3 hours.

SETUP

Position the ice buckets near the patio table. Put one bottle of purified water in each ice bucket. If you want, you can double up and put two bottles in each bucket, just in case, as sometimes the demonstration doesn't work if one of the bottles is accidentally knocked. Pack ice right around the bottles in both buckets and set aside three or four ice cubes in your freezer—you'll need these later. Next, pour a good amount of rock salt over the ice in each bucket, and top up the buckets with water. Stick a thermometer in each bucket and keep an eye on the temperature as the buckets cool. You're waiting for the temperature to drop to 17°F (–8°C). This will probably take around half an hour. Make sure you don't leave it too long or the water may freeze, and you don't want it to—yet! You can keep adding ice and salt as needed so that the bottles stay submerged, but be careful not to knock the bottles when checking on them. When the temperature in the ice buckets reaches 17°F (–8°C), leave them for another 10 minutes.

TESTING

As soon as you're ready, take the side dish and put the ice cubes you previously set aside in the freezer into the bottom of the dish. Then gently pick up one bottle from the ice bucket. Handle it very carefully. Unscrew the lid, taking care not to shake or knock the bottle. Now pour the supercooled water from the bottle onto the ice cubes in the dish. What happens? Flex your creativity to form weird and wonderful ice sculptures. What texture does the ice that forms have?

You'll get the best results if you use deionized water, which is sold for use in car batteries.

INSTANT ICE

ADDITIONAL SETUP

Empty the jug (use a glass if your jug isn't see-through) and place it on the backyard table. Just as carefully as before, take one of the bottles from the ice bucket. Pour the water from the bottle into the jug until it's three-quarters full. Now take one of the ice cubes you set aside and drop it into the center of the liquid. What happens? You probably have a fully frozen jug of water on your hands—instantly! Does it make a difference how large the container of water is?

Take a clean glass and fill it three-quarters full with the supercooled water. Now see what happens if you lightly touch the surface of the water in the glass with one of the ice cubes. You should see the ice crystals spread through the liquid, just as they did when you dropped in the ice cube.

You can also do this experiment with a supercooled bottle of soda. You should see the ice crystals form around bubbles of carbon dioxide that try to escape when you add the ice.

Water freezes at 32°F (0°C), right? So how do we get our bottled water down to 17°F (−8°C) while keeping it liquid? The secret is using purified water. When water freezes normally, the ice crystals establish themselves around impurities and particles in the liquid, in a process called nucleation. Since our purified water does not have these impurities, there is nothing for the ice crystals to form around, so the bottled water stays liquid while becoming supercooled. When you pour the water onto the ice cubes, the cubes form the nucleus needed to start the formation of ice crystals. Likewise, when you drop an ice cube into the supercooled water or touch an ice cube to the water's surface, the ice cube kick-starts the nucleation process. And when you tap the bottle on the table, bubbles in the liquid are the nuclei around which the ice crystals form.

The ice sculptures you create will have a slushy texture. You can pick up the ice and hold it like a watery snowball. It's also pure and deliciously cooling on a hot day—you can even add some of the melted syrup from a freezer pop to make your own snow cones.

NATURE'S COOKIN"

S'mores, anyone?

No matter how hot your oven gets, do not attempt to cook raw food—especially meat—in it. Eating something that's not properly cooked can be really dangerous, so you should stick to stuff that just needs heating/melting, rather than actual cooking.

SETUP

On top of the pizza box, mark a border roughly 2in (5cm) from the edge all the way around. With the penknife, cut along this on three sides, leaving the fourth edge, to create a flap that you can open and close. Line the inside of the box and the flap with tinfoil, with the shiny side facing up. Glue the black paper to the inner base of the box. Lift the flap and tightly cover the opening you cut with plastic wrap, taping it in place. You should still be able to open the box's original lid (which now has a window in it).

TESTING

Open the box and put a piece of food inside, on top of the black paper. Close the lid and open the flap fully, and then position the box in a sunny spot. Use the ruler or length of wood to prop open the foil-covered flap so that as many of the sun's rays as possible are reflected onto the plastic wrap. Now watch what happens. You may need to be patient. Try different foods. You could sandwich marshmallows between cookies to make s'mores.

You can also try adding insulation to the oven. Grab a few rolled-up sheets of newspaper and position these around the edges of your oven inside the pizza box, then try cooking again. Does the insulation make any difference?

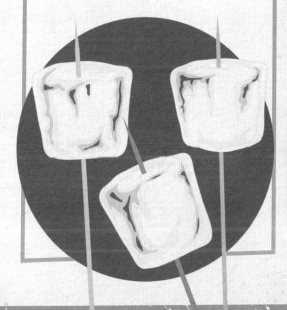

IN CONCLUSION

The sun's rays reflect off the tinfoil lid and travel through the plastic wrap into the homemade "oven." Some sunlight also falls directly through the plastic wrap. The light energy in the inside of the box is transformed into thermal energy, heating up the air trapped inside your oven. The black paper lining absorbs the heat energy from the direct and reflected rays. If you put a thermometer inside the pizza-box oven, on a hot day with no wind you might get a reading of as much as 200°F (93°C).

Of course, solar ovens don't have to be made out of pizza boxes. The technology dates back to the 18th century, and the first successful version was made by Swiss physicist, geologist, and Alpine explorer Horace de Saussure in 1737. Because they are cost-effective, easy-to-make, and environmentally friendly, solar ovens are used today in refugee camps to sterilize water and cook food. They come in many forms, but all have a reflective element to concentrate solar energy, a containing/receiving component to convert solar to thermal energy, and an enclosing design to trap the energy and heat the food.

FIZZIN' COLOR CUBES

Release frozen vinegar's bubbly personality

YOU WILL NEED:
- Vinegar • Baking soda
- Food dye (as many different colors as you want to experiment with)
- Water • Dish soap
- Ice tray • Shallow dish
- Cup or jug

SETUP

Make up a mixture of three parts vinegar to one part water, then add a drop or two of your preferred food dye. You can make up as many different colors as you like by adding different food dyes to different batches of the vinegar/water mixture. Pour this into the ice tray and pop it in the freezer. Next, make up a mixture of three parts baking soda to one part water in a shallow dish, keeping a little back in a cup or jug. You could add a different food dye to this mixture to make for some interesting color combinations later on.

TESTING

This experiment is a bit smelly (from the vinegar) as well as potentially very messy, so choose an area of the backyard where you don't mind making a mess. Once the colored vinegar/water cubes are frozen, take them out of the freezer and get to work. Pop a couple of the color cubes into the water/baking soda mixture. What reaction do you see? What happens to the colors? Try laying out a couple of the colored cubes on the tabletop or the ground and pouring the baking soda mixture directly onto them. What happens this time? Do you see any difference if you pop a color cube into plain water before pouring on the baking soda mixture? How about if you squirt a little dish soap on the color cube?

Look out for unusual ice trays to make interestingly shaped color cubes. How about making heart-shaped ones for Valentine's Day?

IN CONCLUSION

Bubbly bubbly! Vinegar and baking soda produce an acid-base reaction. The sodium bicarbonate (baking soda), a base, reacts with the acetic acid in the vinegar, producing sodium acetate and carbonic acid. Then the carbonic acid breaks up, releasing carbon dioxide gas, which we see as bubbles foaming up in the different versions of the color cube experiment. The fact that we have frozen the vinegar in a mixture with water slows down the reaction, but you'll notice that as the color cube melts, the reaction fizzes up. You'll probably find that dipping the color cube in water before adding the baking soda mix speeds up the reaction. A squirt of dish soap also helps the reaction along.

You could try reversing the experiment, freezing cubes of your baking soda mixture and then putting these into a tray of vinegar and water. Either way, this makes a great little sideshow at a barbecue or summer party if you set it up on a table in the backyard.

GLOSSARY

Bamboozled by terminology? Here's our handy guide to the technical terms used in this book.

Acid/base reaction—a chemical process in which an acid and a base exchange hydrogen ions. They neutralize one another, producing a salt and water.

Adhesion—attraction between molecules of different substances.

Atmospheric pressure (also known as air pressure)—the force exerted on an object by the weight of the air above it. The weight of air is created by gravity pulling the air down to Earth.

Catalyst—an element that speeds up a chemical reaction but is not used up in the reaction.

Centripetal force—the force that attracts an object following a circular path toward the center of the circle it is traveling along. The word comes from the Latin *centrum* (center) and *petere* (to seek), so means center-seeking force.

Cohesion—attraction between molecules of the same substance. For example, water molecules cohere, and this is an important factor in surface tension.

Electrostatics—the study of non-moving electric charges (distinct from electric currents).

Exothermic reaction—a chemical process that releases energy as heat.

Fluidity—a measure of how easily a liquid flows—the opposite of viscosity. Water has high fluidity.

Friction—the force that hinders the movement of two surfaces against one another. For example, friction between the tires and the road slows down your bicycle or car as you travel. This is why you need energy—your legs moving or an engine—to keep moving.

Genetic traits—characteristics determined by genes.

Genome—the complete set of genetic material in any organism.

Gravity—the force of attraction between two bodies with mass. For example, gravity attracts your body toward the center of the Earth; it attracts the Earth and other planets to the sun and holds these planets in their orbits around the sun.

Heavy gas—a dense gas, one that has more mass per square foot than a lighter (less dense) gas. Helium is lighter than air, which is why helium-filled balloons rise. Carbon dioxide is heavier than air.

Inertia—the tendency of objects to resist change, so that they stay still or keep moving at the speed and in the direction they are traveling unless a force interferes. In 1687 Sir Isaac Newton defined inertia as the "power of resisting by which every body, as much as in it lies, endeavors to preserve its present state, whether it be of rest or of moving uniformly forward in a straight line."

Nucleation—the initial process in the formation of a crystal in a liquid or gas. A nucleation site is a point where nucleation may occur.

Nucleic acids—large molecules that carry genetic information. Deoxyribonucleic acid (DNA) and ribonucleic acid (RNA) are types of nucleic acid. Nucleic acids are so called because scientists first thought they existed only in the nucleus of cells, but they have since been found elsewhere, for example, in cells with no nucleus, such as bacteria.

Organosilicon compounds—organic compounds containing carbon–silicon bonds.

Polymer—large molecule made up of long chains of repeating units.

Potential energy—energy stored in an object due to its position or internal stress. For example, a stretched rubber band has its elastic potential energy released when it is let go.

Precipitation—the formation of a solid from a solution.

Refraction—deflection of light, radio, or sound waves as they pass from one medium to another, for example, from air into glass.

Salt—a substance produced by the reaction of an acid with a base.

Solvent—a substance, usually a liquid, that dissolves other materials (called solutes) to form a solution.

Supercooling—bringing a gas or liquid to below its freezing point without it becoming a solid.

Surface tension—tension on the surface of a liquid. On the surface of water, the water molecules are attracted more to the water molecules beneath and alongside them than to the air molecules above, and this causes the water to form a surface-like membrane.

Thermal conduction—transfer of heat between solids, where heat is transferred through physical contact. Some materials (e.g. metals, especially copper and silver) are good conductors of heat; others (e.g. plastics and wood) do not transfer heat well.

Transpiration—the loss of water from a plant, principally through stomates (small groups of cells that act like pores) on the surface of leaves.

Viscosity—the measure of how much a liquid resists flowing (the opposite of fluidity). Treacle, for example, has high viscosity.

Vortex—a mass of fluid or gas spiraling around a central axis.

FURTHER READING

BOOKS

Akiyama, Lance. *Launchers, Lobbers, and Rockets Engineer: Make 20 Awesome Ballistic Blasters with Ordinary Stuff*. Beverly, MA: Rockport Publishers, 2018.

Beattie, Rob. *Kitchen Sink Science*. New York, NY: Metro Books, 2019.

Downie, Neil A. *The Ultimate Book of Saturday Science: The Very Best Backyard Science Experiments You Can Do Yourself*. Princeton, NJ: Princeton University Press, 2012.

Gurstelle, William. *Backyard Ballistics: Build Potato Cannons, Paper Match Rockets, Cincinnati Fire Kites, Tennis Ball Mortars, and More Dynamite Devices*. Chicago, IL: Chicago Review Press, 2012.

Naked Scientists, The. *Boom! 50 Fantastic Science Experiments to Try at Home with Your Kids*. East Petersburg, PA: IMM Lifestyle, 2016.

Scheckel, Larry. *Ask a Science Teacher: 250 Answers to Questions You've Always Had About How Everyday Stuff Really Works*. New York, NY: The Experiment LLC, 2014.

Winston, Robert. *Home Lab: Exciting Experiments for Budding Scientists*. London: DK, 2016.

WEBSITES

BBC Science www.bbc.co.uk/science

Exploratorium www.exploratorium.edu

Explorit www.explorit.org

Incredible Science www.incrediblescience.com

Inspiration Laboratories inspirationlaboratories.com

Instructables www.instructables.com

Khan Academy www.khanacademy.org

Live Science www.livescience.com

Naked Scientists www.thenakedscientists.com

NASA: What is a Black Hole? www.nasa.gov/audience/forstudents/k-4/stories/nasa-knows/what-is-a-black-hole-k4.html

New Scientist www.newscientist.com

Physics.Org www.physics.org

Physics Central www.physicscentral.com/experiment/physicsathome

Physics Central: Physics Buzz physicsbuzz.physicscentral.com

Popular Science www.popsci.com

Science: How Stuff Works science.howstuffworks.com

Science Learning Hub www.sciencelearn.org.nz

Science Sparks www.science-sparks.com

Science: Wonder How To science.wonderhowto.com

Sciencing.com sciencing.com/physics

Scientific American: Bring Science Home www.scientificamerican.com/
education/bring-science-home

Sciphile sciphile.org

Steve Spangler Science www.stevespanglerscience.com

The Backyard Scientist www.youtube.com/user/TheBackyardScientist

The Kids Should See This thekidshouldseethis.com—this site links to a neat
video of building the Self-Supporting Bridge (see page 112)

The Physics Classroom www.physicsclassroom.com

UCSB ScienceLine: Physics Questions scienceline.ucsb.edu/searchtopic.
php?category=physics

University of Wisconsin-Madison: Experiments You Can Do at Home
scifun.chem.wisc.edu/wop/homeexpphys.html

**University of Wisconsin-Madison: The Wonders of Physics Traveling
Outreach Program** wonders.physics.wisc.edu

WikiHow www.wikihow.com

TV AND RADIO

Backyard Science www.abc.net.au/tv/programs/backyard-science

NPR Science www.npr.org/sections/science

The Surfing Scientist www.abc.net.au/science/surfingscientist

PUZZLER ANSWERS

p.29: The theory of gravitation—reputedly inspired by seeing an apple fall from a tree.

p.45: You give the rubber bands their potential energy when you stretch them.

p.53: False. It's a misconception that draining water always spins clockwise in the northern
hemisphere and counterclockwise in the southern hemisphere. It can spin either way or
go straight down.

p.67: True. They form just like clouds, but at/near ground level.

p.70: Try reflecting light from a CD.

p.101: It's Latin for "room." Camera obscura just means "dark room."

p.125: True—Swedish scientist Emanuel Swedenborg experimented with the idea in 1716.

p.128: True—in fact, it would reach to the sun and back 300 times!

INDEX

NOTES